PAGE
10

PAGE
42

PAGE
84

FICTION

PAGE 110

PAGE 142

PAGE 168

PAGE 89

DC Thomson

Love Is All Around

Pets aren't just for Christmas – they are loyal and loving companions all year round, as many of our favourite celebrities will happily testify…

Missing you already!

Holly Willoughby

Holly dreads leaving her beloved Siamese cat Roxy when she goes on holiday with her family. "I hate saying goodbye to Roxy, which is why I tend to ring my cat-sitter more than my parents when we're away," admitted Holly.

Katherine Jenkins

When Katherine is at her family home in Wales, she loves going walking in a nearby beauty spot with her mum's dog, Lily. "Lily is very cute and loveable," said Katherine, who also revealed that she likes to relax last thing at night by watching television and playing with Lily.

Couch companion

John Barrowman

"During a visit to Cardiff Dogs Home, I fell in love with a 12-week-old Jack Russell Terrier who had been abandoned in an empty flat," reveals John, who has two other rescue dogs, Harris and Charlie. "I adopted the little fella and Captain Jack is now part of our family."

Will the real Captain Jack stand up?

Part of the family

Gloria Hunniford

Gloria's children grew up with dogs, cats and rabbits and Gloria now has a King Charles Spaniel, Gemma. When asked to name the love of her life, Gloria replied: "My husband, my children and grandchildren, and my lovely dog, Gemma."

More Overleaf

Paul O'Grady

"I like being surrounded by animals," says Paul, whose farm in Kent is also home to his three dogs, two giant pigs, eight cows, a lamb, three goats, a horse, chickens, donkeys, a love bird and a flock of geese!

Lots of company!

Martin Clunes

"Animals give you a sense of belonging," explained Martin, who lives on a farm with his wife and daughter and their horses, dogs, chickens, sheep and cats. "We're always taking long walks with the dogs and when my horse leans its big head down to mine, there's this real connection."

Feels a connection

Alesha Dixon

"Pets bring us so much happiness and deserve the very best care in return," says Alesha, who shares her home with three dogs, Daisy, Roxy and Rosy. "My favourite way to relax is going out with my dogs to clear my mind and take in all that lovely fresh air."

Fresh air and happiness

Waifs and strays welcome

Sharon Osbourne

Sharon can't say no to a dog looking for a new home – which has led to the number of dogs in the Osbourne household rocketing to 16! "Word's got out in LA that anyone who finds a stray dog should call the Osbournes!" Sharon joked.

By best-selling novelist

Trisha Ashley

· ·

Not Just For Christmas

Prepare to have your heartstrings tugged as a young couple's differing priorities threaten to ruin the festivities

No," Nick said firmly, setting his jaw and crossing his arms over his chest in the darkly brooding and very Mr Darcy way that Rosie usually found extremely attractive. "We can't possibly have another dog – two are more than enough!"

"But Nick, one more won't make that much difference," she pleaded. "And poor Tiggy's been in the kennels for over a year now, just because he isn't the prettiest of dogs. No one ever seems to see beyond that to his lovely nature."

Rosie was a veterinary nurse, but she also often volunteered at a pet rescue centre on Saturday mornings, which was

"What? You told them that without consulting me?" he demanded angrily. "I'm very fond of Jimmy and Flo, you know that, but the costs mount up, what with micro-chipping, insurance, food, and kennels if we go away – and we're supposed to be saving up for a house deposit, remember?"

"Then what about your flying lessons? They cost an absolute fortune!" she retaliated. "If you can have an expensive hobby like that, I don't see why I can't have another dog."

"Flying is something I'd always wanted to do," he retorted defensively. "I told you so, the first time we went out together –

"I've said that if no one offers Tiggy a home in a month, I'll take him…"

where Jimmy and Flo, her two Jack Russell terriers, had come from. But since she'd already adopted them before she met and became engaged to Nick, it had been a case of "love me, love my dogs."

"Anyway," she added defiantly, since Nick's expression was showing no sign of softening, "I've already told them that if no one else offers Tiggy a home by the end of January, I'll take him."

and you told me about your dogs, but you never said then that you intended to have a whole pack of them."

"I don't think you can call three a pack," Rosie said coldly.

"Well, I'm sick of coming second to the ones we do have," he snapped. Then, somehow, the argument just spiralled until in the end Rosie packed her stuff

Continued overleaf…

Rosie and her beloved dogs came as a package

and the dogs into her car and flounced off to stay with her Great Aunt Emily.

Since her mother had remarried and gone to live in Spain, Rosie had taken to spending Christmas at Aunt Emily's rambling old cottage in a village a few miles away anyway, where she and the dogs were always sure of a welcome.

Of course, Aunt Emily had invited Nick to spend Christmas with them too this year, and had been looking forward to meeting him, so she was going to be very disappointed about that.

However, Aunt Emily had an elderly springer spaniel of her own, so Rosie was sure she would sympathise with her about Nick's hard-heartedness.

But to Rosie's surprise, Aunt Emily said she could see both sides of the argument and they were equally valid.

"I do deeply sympathise about poor Tiggy," she assured Rosie, "but I do think that since you are engaged, you should have discussed the matter with Nick first, before you definitely said you would take on the dog. I am sure you could have persuaded him, if you had gone the right way about it."

Rosie, now her first anger had cooled, had been coming to much the same conclusion – though she wasn't going to admit as much to anyone, and especially not to Nick!

"I don't see why I should have to, when he spends all that money on flying lessons!" she said stubbornly.

"But it is good for a man to have a hobby, and he usually has the lessons on Saturdays when you are at the rescue kennels, doesn't he? So you both spend time doing what you most want to. And flying…" Aunt Emily paused and an oddly dreamy, reminiscent smile crossed

Great Aunt Emily had loved her wartime flying years

her face. "Flying is such wonderful fun!"

Rosie stared at her small, elderly, silver-haired aunt in astonishment. "You mean – you would have liked to have learned to fly?" she asked tentatively.

"I did fly," Aunt Emily said, her blue eyes twinkling with amusement. "I know you think I've spent my entire life here in the village, going to WI meetings and knitting, but I was a young woman during the war and we all had jobs to do! Mine was in the Air Transport Auxiliary. I was an Attagirl!"

"An Attagirl?" Rosie repeated, puzzled.

"That's what we became known as. There were over a hundred women among the pilots who flew the new planes to the airbases, and damaged planes back for repair – and we could fly anything from a Spitfire to a Lancaster.

"Spitfires were my favourite – they were wonderful planes," Emily said enthusiastically. Rosie suddenly saw her as the eager, brave young girl she had been during those difficult wartime years.

"I'm amazed," Rosie confessed. "But why on earth have you never told me about it before?"

"I loved flying so much that after the war I couldn't bear even to think about it, because I couldn't afford to carry on. My father – your grandfather – had been killed fire-watching during an air raid, so I had to help support my mother and my younger sister."

Emily unearthed some photograph albums and showed Rosie pictures of smartly uniformed young women and men, standing next to a variety of aircraft. In fact, in one a recognisable but dark-haired and youthful Great Aunt Emily was actually sitting astride the nose of a small plane, wearing a jaunty peaked hat and waving!

Rosie couldn't help thinking how fascinated Nick would be by all of it.

In fact, it looked as if the worst elements of every known breed of dog had gone into his making.

"And she chose you over me?" Nick said aloud, incredulously.

Something in the tone of his voice made the little dog flatten his ears (what was left of them), hang his tail and slink off into the furthest corner of his concrete pen, trembling. Nick immediately felt horribly guilty.

"Poor old Tiggy," commented a passing kennel maid. "Some dogs just hate being in kennels, and he's been here so long. He's a lovely dog really; looks aren't everything, are they? But luckily for him, if he doesn't find a new home by the end of January, one of the girls who volunteer to work here has promised she is going to adopt him."

"Yes – I know, actually," he told her. "I'm Rosie's fiancé."

He might have added that he was not too keen on the idea of adopting another

He wasn't sure about his status as fiance any more – Tiggy was his last hope

Meanwhile sheer curiosity (and a slightly guilty conscience) had driven Nick to visit the Happy Paws dog rescue centre, where he was now eyeing the rival for Rosie's affections through the thick wire mesh.

When Rosie had told him Tiggy was not the prettiest dog ever, she'd been wildly over-estimating his attractions, for Tiggy was the least prepossessing mutt he'd ever seen in his entire life!

He was small, with rough brown fur, a squished face, most of one ear missing and a bent tail. He also had short, bandy legs and a disproportionately long body.

dog, especially the ragamuffin one in front of him – or even that he wasn't too sure any more about his status as Rosie's fiancé either. But just then Tiggy turned his head and gave him another shivering, pleading look from his round, dark eyes.

Something came over Nick and to his horror, he heard his voice saying, "Actually, I know she's really fallen for him, so I wondered if I could take him home with me now, as a surprise Christmas present?"

"Really?" Her face lit up eagerly. "Of course, we don't usually rehome dogs **Continued overleaf…**

just before Christmas, but in this case… brilliant! Come on!"

And before he knew it, Tiggy was signed over to him and he'd spent a small fortune on a collar, lead, food and a cosy new dog-bed.

He wasn't sure how Rosie's other two dogs were going to feel about the disreputable new arrival – assuming Rosie took him back, of course! – but he thought Tiggy might just do the trick.

And since Rosie's Aunt Emily had called him that day and informed him in no uncertain terms that she still expected him to arrive on Christmas Eve as they had arranged, despite the quarrel, he would have the perfect opportunity.

Meanwhile, he and Tiggy had a few days to learn to get on together… or not.

He glanced over his shoulder before pulling out of the car park to find that Tiggy was curled up on the parcel shelf like a slightly grotesque nodding dog.

He looked slightly less cowed and, as their eyes met, his tail tentatively and bravely thumped a couple of times.

they were saving up for as a wedding present from her!

"So perhaps now that problem is out of the way, you needn't resent the cost of Nick's flying lessons," Aunt Emily continued. "And equally, he may be more accommodating about the dog. But if not, I will take him – he'll be good company for Patch."

The old spaniel, who was lying in a comfortable, snoring heap before the fire with Rosie's two dogs, half-opened his eyes at the sound of his name but then drifted back to sleep again.

"It's very kind of you, Aunt Emily, but actually, since Nick hasn't contacted me at all since we argued, there clearly isn't going to be a wedding!"

"Silly me," Aunt Emily said, but only a moment later she was asking if she had remembered to put out fresh towels in the room she'd prepared for Nick, and whether the whisky she'd bought was the right kind that he liked.

All in all, Rosie thought glumly, it looked set to be the worst Christmas ever

Aunt Emily seemed to be losing the plot. She was still convinced Nick was coming

By Christmas Eve, Rosie had given up any hope that Nick would contact her to say he was sorry – and she was far too proud and stubborn to beg him to have her back.

Also, she had a new worry, for she was beginning to suspect that Aunt Emily, who had always been as sharp as a tack, was beginning to lose the plot. She'd been talking as if she still expected Nick to turn up later, and now she had just cheerily informed her that she and Nick could have the rest of the house deposit

– but she would just have to try and put a brave face on it!

Aunt Emily was expecting someone round for drinks later, so when the doorbell rang and she said, "Could you just get that, darling, while I go into the kitchen and warm the mince pies?" Rosie got up and opened the front door, ready to welcome one of her aunt's elderly friends from the village.

Instead, she found herself staring at Nick, who was standing on the doorstep, feathery flakes of white snow flecking his

How would Jimmy and Flo take to the new arrival?

dark hair. For a minute she thought her eyes were playing tricks on her, by showing her exactly what she really wanted to see. But even after she blinked vigorously he was still there, looking gravely down at her.

"Hello, Rosie."

"What on earth are you doing here?"

"Aunt Emily called me and insisted I come," he told her. "And actually, I wanted a chance to tell you I'm really, really sorry I was so horrible and unreasonable to you – and to give you your Christmas present."

"I'm really sorry too," Rosie admitted. "Once I'd talked to Aunt Emily, I started to see things a bit differently. Oh – and I've found out something about Aunt Emily you'll find fascinating: she flew planes in the war!"

Then she broke off, registering for the first time that he was holding in his arms a small bundle wrapped in a tartan blanket – and it was wriggling.

Out popped a familiar, ugly head on a wrinkled neck that was adorned with a jaunty red bow.

"Tiggy!" she cried.

But Tiggy barely spared her a glance. Instead he was looking adoringly up into Nick's face.

"Well, there's gratitude for you," said Nick with a sudden grin. "I brought him as your Christmas present, but actually he's such a character I don't think I can part with him. He tried to eat the sofa cushions the first night I took him home, and now he won't let me out of his sight," he added dotingly.

Rosie felt a pang – almost of jealousy – and suddenly she understood how Nick must feel when he heard her talking so affectionately to the other two dogs. But then she laughed.

Nick came into the hall and put Tiggy down. He sauntered sedately past them, while the other dogs yapped excitedly from behind the sitting room door.

"But if I can't part with him, you'll have to take us both," Nick said hopefully, putting his arms around her. "And you know what they say: a dog isn't just for Christmas – and neither am I."

"No, you're forever," agreed Rosie and gave him a kiss.

"Attagirl," said Emily's voice approvingly. "Now, shut that door before all the warm air escapes, and come into the sitting room. I think this calls for a small celebration!"

TRISHA ASHLEY INTERVIEW
Turn the page to enjoy a cosy chat with the author herself!

ILLUSTRATIONS: BEVERLEY YOUNG, JAMES DEWAR

Trisha Ashley

Favourite My Weekly author reveals what makes her laugh, cry and be inspired

Trisha is inspired by both sea and countryside

What inspires my writing
Food, friendship and gardening are all strong inspirational threads. I also find the lovely countryside of West Lancashire, with its traditions, ancient houses and market towns, is a fertile source of ideas.

Where I write my novels
Mainly in my study upstairs, a tiny boxroom with a lovely view of the sea. The Great Orme of Llandudno is to the right and Puffin Island and Anglesey to the left.

My Lancashire heritage gives me a dark sense of humour and I love quirky things

What makes me laugh
I always say that part of my Lancashire heritage is my dark sense of humour in adversity – it's like a lifebelt keeping me afloat as I sweep through the sea of life. I love odd, quirky things but find slapstick comedy painfully unfunny.

What makes me cry
The TV news, very often, if I see sadness and suffering. I also cry every time I watch *Love Actually* and see Emma Thompson's character bravely putting on a cheerful face for the children, after learning of her husband's betrayal – so moving.

How I relax in my spare time
I walk the dog on the beach, though that isn't always relaxing! I like to sew crazy patchwork gifts for friends and also paint in oils whenever I have time.

When I feel happiest
Last Christmas my novel, *Twelve Days of Christmas*, had been in the Sunday Times bestseller list for four weeks, and then, when my son arrived safely home for Christmas, just before the terrible snow shut down the roads, I found myself thinking, "Life doesn't get any better than this, Trisha!"

Teatime Treat

MAKE A TASTY PUD!

Toffee Apple Tasty Slice

FRUITY & JUICY

Ingredients

- 250g (9oz) light brown sugar
- 150g (5oz) butter
- 150g (5oz) canned caramel or dulce de leche + extra for serving
- 2 medium eggs, beaten
- 200g (7oz) self-raising flour
- 2 eating apples, peeled, cored and chopped
- 1 eating apple, peeled, cored and thinly sliced into rings
- Scoops of vanilla ice-cream

Preparation time: 20mins plus cooling time
Cooking time: 1hr 5mins
Serves: 6

- Pre-heat the oven to 180°C, Fan Oven 160°C, Gas Mark 4. Grease and line a 20cm (8inch) square cake tin. Put the **sugar**, **butter** and **caramel** in a saucepan and place over a low heat. Heat gently, stirring occasionally, until melted and smooth. Cool for 10mins.
- Stir in the **eggs**, **flour** and **chopped apple**. Spoon into the prepared tin and smoothe the top. Arrange **apple rings** on top and bake for about 1hr until risen and just set. Cool for 20mins before cutting into slices. Best served warm with extra **caramel** poured on top and a generous scoop of **ice-cream**!

RECIPES: KATHRYN HAWKINS PHOTOGRAPHY: UPFRONT PHOTOGRAPHY

His Shining Star

In an instant their perfect world was shattered – but with the help of her son, Ginnie knew they could survive

By Jenny Curtis

T ime for school, Toby!" Ginnie clicked the shutter, a smile lighting her face as she watched her six-year-old son, shrieking with excitement, scoop up a handful of snow and wrestle with his dad, trying to put it down his neck.

Matt obligingly let out a shout of mock terror and then swooped to pick Toby up, swinging him high in the air.

That would make a great picture, Ginnie thought to herself. Such a shame to spoil their fun, but Matt had to get to work, too. "Hey, you!" she spluttered, laughing as an unexpected snowball caught her on the face. "That was wet!"

pulled Ginnie towards him, "and you, my lovely wife, make sure you have a good dinner waiting for me when I come home." He nuzzled into her neck. "And it could be your lucky night."

"You reckon?" Ginnie's eyes sparkled, holding him close, savouring the moment.

"Get to work, you chancer…" she playfully pushed him away, "and earn us some money, then!"

It was a short walk to Toby's school.

"Hold tight to my hand," Ginnie instructed, "the pavement's quite slippery." She smiled to herself, picturing Matt driving into town, listening absently to Toby's chatter. She would cook something special tonight, get a bottle of wine – she could even put on her little

She would cook something special for them tonight, get a bottle of wine…

She picked off the snow and threw it back at a gleeful Toby. "Come on, you monster. Let's get going."

Ginnie grabbed his gloved hand as he ran past her. "If we hurry, you'll be able to make a snowman in the playground with your friends."

"Don't think there'll be enough for that." Matt dried his hands. "Right, I'd better get going. Have a fun day. Toby…" He planted a kiss on his son's head, and

black dress; she hadn't worn that for ages.

"There you go." Toby shrugged off her quick hug, eager to get to the playground where lots of children were already making the most of the night's snowfall. "Be good. Love you, baby."

B ack home, Ginnie turned on the radio, made a coffee and started to write a shopping list before changing to go to the supermarket where she worked

"Look for the brightest star, Toby"

part-time. The doorbell made her jump – ah, the postman, probably the book she'd ordered for Matt for Christmas.

She opened the door with a smile of anticipation on her face. It wasn't the postman. It was a policeman and woman.

"May we come in?" …and in that instant her whole world was shattered.

There was a roaring in her ears, like **Continued overleaf…**

surf in a storm. She looked blankly at the grave faces. What were they saying? She could see their mouths moving but couldn't make any sense of the words.

Someone was screaming. "No! No..." She realised it was her own voice, her heart pounding so hard it hurt. She couldn't breathe. Her legs had turned to water; she felt herself falling.

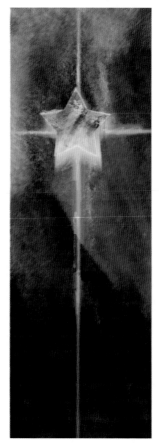

It seemed a long time later she was sitting in a chair, icy cold, feeling sick and drained, a steaming mug placed in hands that were shaking so much she couldn't hold it properly.

"Is there someone we can call for you?" the policeman asked gently.

Ginnie obediently took a sip of the sweet tea, looking out of the window, looking anywhere but at their apologetic eyes, noticing the sun was shining, the snow had all gone.

Toby would be so disappointed... and then it hit her, like a bolt of lightning shooting through her; the pain unbearable. Oh, God – it was all true. Ice on the road, head-on collision, tragic accident. Matt dead.

Looking back three weeks later, she couldn't believe that she'd got through it – all so unreal, a bad dream that she didn't seem able to wake up from. The still, silent Matt looking so normal lying in the hospital, his distraught parents, clinging to her – the funeral, all the sympathetic, caring faces, so many people who had loved him.

Trying to explain to a white-faced Toby that his daddy had gone to heaven, but would always love him and watch over him.

"But where is he? Where is heaven?" Toby was cuddled up on her lap, looking out of the window at a gleaming moon in the dark sky.

Ginnie took a deep breath. "You see all the stars? Now look for the brightest one…"

Toby strained his eyes. "Yes, yes – I can see it – that one, over there!"

"Well, that's your daddy, making sure you're safe and smiling down at you."

She hugged him to her, struggling to hold back the tears – she so wanted to believe it herself.

It was Toby's letter to Father Christmas, asking for just one present – his daddy to come back – that broke her. She'd tried so hard to be strong.

The huge sobs tore at her. She buried her face in Matt's dressing-gown – how was she going to get through Christmas, carry on without him?

The school was preparing for their Nativity play, Toby was going to be one of the Three Kings. Ginnie made him a cloak out of a velvet curtain and cut out a cardboard crown which he painted gold, his tongue peeping out as he carefully stuck on coloured beads, and practised his lines.

"I'm taking frankincense to the baby Jesus," he said importantly. "What's frankincense, Mummy?"

"It's a special perfume, very expensive. Jesus will love it." Ginnie rubbed her eyes tiredly. How she wished she could just go

"That was for Jesus," the boy said accusingly, then scuttled to the side and stood stiffly, his job done.

Ginnie clutched her mother-in-law's hand as a beaming Toby marched on carrying a brass pot.

"Have you come far?" Mary busily unwrapped the shawl from her baby and inspected its nappy.

"I travelled all night following the star."

"I know where it is – I know where all Daddy's special things are kept"

to sleep and not wake up… but then Toby was shaking her.

"Mummy, help – the beads won't stick."

She picked him up and held him tight, taking comfort from his warmth. "We need some of Daddy's special glue, don't we?"

"I know where it is – I know where all Daddy's special things are; he told me." He climbed off her lap and ran excitedly to the bureau.

Oh Matt. Matt, I miss you so much.

Matt's mother was going with her to the performance – it was going to be hard for both of them, the first of the many school activities without him.

They sat in the school hall filled with proud families, the tableau set up ready on the stage with fidgeting shepherds and a donkey looking suspiciously like a reindeer waiting for the Kings to arrive.

A determined Mary sat upright violently rocking her baby, ignoring the prods from the elbow of an embarrassed Joseph as the first King in a tartan blanket crept up, and shyly handed her his present of a gold bracelet.

"Have you come far?" Mary asked, admiring the bracelet on her wrist.

Toby pointed up to the big gold star hanging above them, watching interestedly as she tutted and adjusted the nappy. Ginnie felt tears pricking the back of her eyes – he was word perfect.

"Oh, how nice." Mary re-wrapped Jesus neatly and proceeded to bang him on the back. "And where is my present?"

Toby was staring up at the star intently, his forehead creased in a frown.

"You're supposed to give me a present," Mary insisted crossly.

A huge smile suddenly lit up Toby's face as he turned to her. "That star…" his voice was loud and clear, "that star – it's like my daddy – he showed me."

He gazed into the audience until his shining eyes found Ginnie. She smiled at him brilliantly through her tears. She and her son. Together they would be all right; together they would find the way.

A WORD FROM THE AUTHOR

"We lost my son's dad when he was fifteen. This is how I imagined a little boy, and his mum, would cope at Christmas."

A New Dawn

Amid the Coronation celebrations, you'll feel for Margaret – left to cope alone for a second time without her husband

By Brenda Crickmar

And now, as this radiant young woman of only twenty-five flashes her brilliant smile and waves to the crowds – many of whom have been waiting long hours to see her – we find ourselves at the beginning of a new dawn."

A new dawn, thought Margaret. Yes, the commentator had picked a good phrase to describe the future of a nation. Giving a small sigh, she tried to raise her sagging shoulders and summon some enthusiasm. It seemed like an enormous effort. Life lately felt so very difficult.

Then her glance softened as she turned towards her middle-aged neighbour, who had done everything to make them welcome on this special day.

"Lovely television, Dorothy," she said.

The woman beamed, gratified.

glance at the profile of her twelve-year-old daughter, Jennifer. With her dark hair and intelligent expression, Jennifer was very much her father's daughter. She looked excited now, every bit of her caught up in the romance of the young princess travelling towards Westminster Abbey and her destiny to become the second Queen Elizabeth.

"All right, Mum?" Jennifer asked without moving her head or taking her eyes from the screen.

"Of course," answered Margaret with a cheerfulness she was far from feeling. Briefly she wished that her daughter were older so that she could explain things to her properly. So that they could discuss between them the situation they found themselves in.

But how could you say to a twelve-year-old who, because of the war, had only known her father since she was six,

Graham had made it home from the war. But he wasn't the man she'd married

"Well, we were thinking of getting one anyway and with the Coronation coming up, we decided to break the habit of a lifetime and get it on the never-never."

Never-never, thought Margaret. *The story of my life, really. The life that never actually happens.* She switched her eyes from the black and white grainy picture on her neighbour's small television set, to

that he had gone – not for six months as Margaret had at first pretended, but probably for ever?

Goodness knows, when Graham had eventually been demobbed in 1946, it had been difficult enough to get Jennifer used to the idea of a father who was no longer absent. Sometimes Margaret was to wonder whether his delay in returning to them had been by accident or design.

I must give him time, she'd told herself over and over again.

But Jennifer was not so patient. "Why is Dad always so cross?" she'd asked, an expression of bewilderment on her face. "And why doesn't he want to play cricket with me, like they do next door? Sometimes I don't think he even likes me."

Continued overleaf…

She'd assumed their reunion would be happy

"You have to give him time, love," said Margaret. "The war takes its toll. We all have to adjust. We're really very lucky to have got him back." Then she'd folded her lips, because sometimes she didn't feel very lucky. Graham's continual bad temper had a way of rubbing off. "Now clear up your painting things, you know your dad can't abide a mess."

"And that's another thing," Jennifer muttered darkly. "You never used to mind about a bit of mess."

"Cup of tea, Margaret?"

Jerking herself back to the present, Margaret smiled her thanks to Dorothy, accepted a cup of the hot, reviving liquid and tried to concentrate on the Coronation.

Princess Elizabeth had reached the abbey now, and the full glory of her Coronation dress could be seen. Jennifer's gaze was glued to the screen, an expression of wonderment on her face. For months now, she'd been cutting out the newspaper pictures of both princesses, Elizabeth and Margaret, and pasting them into a scrapbook.

Despite the austerity of the post-war years, the people were embracing the moment, determined to make the most of the momentous occasion. There had been a Coronation party at the school where Margaret worked as secretary, and she'd watched with tender eyes as the children enjoyed their jelly and ice-cream. Later, almost delirious with the idea of their teachers helping to serve party food and making jokes, the children had made their way home with their presentation green Coronation mugs, shouting, "Yo-ho-ho and a bottle of rum".

Graham had watched from behind drawn curtains and a haze of cigarette smoke. "Young hooligans," he'd growled. "They should show some respect."

Margaret wondered if that was the comment that tried her patience too far. "Graham," she'd said. "They're having a bit of fun. What's wrong with that?"

"They haven't seen the things I've seen. Hungry children, starving children." Her husband stared back at her

Amid the austerity, people were eager to celebrate

out of dark, haunted, resentful eyes.

"No, they haven't. But Graham, our children are our future. Don't take away their childhood – it's very precious."

Graham's answer had been to stamp out of the room and down to the pub.

And now he'd gone. She had to face it. Over a month ago, he'd left a note that made it clear he'd gone for good. And, although Margaret wasn't sure whether it was the memory of the pre-war Graham she missed, not the silent, moody stranger he'd become, she felt the void and the lonely sensation of being a single parent once again.

Margaret continued to stare at the

future… We'll just have to see, love."

And why did you say that? she asked herself. She had two choices; she knew that. One was to continue to bluff it out. To somehow manage on her school secretary's pay and pretend that Graham was coming back. Sooner or later the kindly neighbours, and the ones who were not quite so well-intentioned, would stop asking. Jennifer seemed already to be blossoming without the crippling presence that Graham had become.

The other choice – sometimes, it seemed to Margaret, the easier choice – was to pack up and go home to Wales, to a caring family who had never really approved of her marrying Graham, but

She could keep pretending, or go home where "I told you so" hung in the air

screen. The new Queen, her heavy crown weighing on her head, looked fragile and young. Her expression was solemn; her hands holding the sceptre and orb, small and childlike. She was surely too young and inexperienced for the enormous task that confronted her.

One by one, dignitaries including Winston Churchill came up to her gilded throne and pledged allegiance. Her face was serious as she received them; maybe it was only now that she recognised the full enormity of her situation.

"Mum, d'you think we could ever afford a television?" asked Jennifer. "There's lots of programmes I'd like to watch, and I'm sure you would too. And Dad – when he comes home again."

Margaret felt her lips tighten. "Not at the moment," she said shortly. Then, seeing Jennifer's disappointed face, she added, "But maybe some time in the

where the words "we told you so" would, though never uttered, lie heavy in the air.

Return home, tail between her legs? No – she didn't want to do that. Well, no one would. But to manage on her own? Surely that would be an impossibility.

You did it before, said a small voice at the back of her mind. *You managed for five and a half years without a man – without Graham.* But then, of course, so did plenty of other women. They managed alone, just hoping that their man would return home safe from the war; never doubting for a moment that the home-coming, when it happened, would be a truly joyous occasion – a reason for celebration.

Not in Margaret's case, though. The Graham who had courted her, married her, kissed her goodbye, gone off to war vanished from her sight until the war

Continued overleaf…

ended, had disappeared as surely as though he'd been lost in battle.

"Hello, Mags," he'd said on his return. And he'd sounded the same, looked the same – on the outside – anyway.

But inside, he was different. Restless, given to sudden moods and rages. Difficult. And he couldn't keep a job.

"What about teaching?" suggested Margaret. "They're crying out for teachers. With your education, you could teach unqualified for a couple of years and with my secretarial post, we could manage. You could go on a teachers' training course, I'm sure."

Graham gave her a cold stare.

"When I want your advice, Margaret, I'll ask for it. Is that understood?"

Margaret had nodded meekly. She'd still clung on to the thought, then, that time would eventually heal everything. But how much time did you give someone before you gave up on them?

She reflected now on the years of trying to make things work. The incessant smoking; half-finished cigarette ends left smouldering away on the edges of her willow-patterned saucers. Trying to ignore the fact that they'd grown into two very different people, with Graham unable to hold down a job and drinking

Margaret and Jennifer would be better off without him.

At first she'd been heartbroken, then ashamed that somehow she'd failed him. But finally she'd been angry that Graham could find it in himself to just walk away from his responsibilities.

Despite knowing that he was only one of many soldiers back from the war who found they couldn't settle again to civilian life, only one of many who found domestic life and a nine-to-five job too much to cope with, she felt let down and very alone. It was funny, she thought, how no one had thought to ask how the wives of these returning soldiers felt about having their lives disrupted by the return of their menfolk.

So Graham had gone. But Margaret still thought about him, still worried about him, just as she had during the war years. Sometimes she wondered bitterly whether he had ever worried about her and Jennifer with the same intensity.

The television picture was blurred now. Partly through the rain, but mainly because of the unshed tears that were accumulating rapidly behind Margaret's quivering eyelids.

The rain was pelting down in the Mall, bouncing off the pavements, but the

Hanging from a lamp post, waving and laughing, was a tall, dark-haired man

too much, and Margaret, against all her instincts, rapidly becoming the stronger partner of the two.

In the end Graham had been the one to give up. The message, propped up against the old brown china tea pot, had been brief. He'd tried, really he had, but felt he'd rather be a free agent and that

crowds didn't seem to care. They were cheering and shouting, wrapping themselves in the red, white and blue bunting that was festooned everywhere. Some of them were climbing the lampposts. The camera shots lingered on the crowds lining the Mall.

"Mum," said Jennifer suddenly, turning

He was haunted by what he'd seen

carriages, the brass bands. A pale, watery sun made a brief appearance; the crowds began to roar and run as if with one mind towards the gates of Buckingham Palace.

The new young Queen had appeared on the balcony. She was smiling with relief, her eyes full of hope and confidence for the future. Her own, and that of the nation.

Her Majesty's smile was contagious. Margaret felt the corners of her mouth begin to twitch and then a small lurch under her ribcage as her heart lifted with hope. Suddenly she was aware that she was smiling widely.

The future was full of possibilities. It belonged to everyone. The new Queen, the jubilant crowds, Graham, Jennifer – and, yes, even Margaret.

She was still a relatively young woman and yes, things might be tough, but they'd managed to make a life together, her and Jennifer between them.

If Graham were to come back, yes, they would try again; if not – well, life would go on without him. Somehow she'd cope. It would be easier, now that she had that last picture of him, alive and well and swinging from a lamppost, to treasure in her mind's eye.

But the future beckoned. She straightened her shoulders, caught Jennifer's eye, grinned and winked.

For after all – today was the beginning of a new dawn.

her head in Margaret's direction.

But Margaret wasn't listening. She stared at the small screen and drew in her breath. Hanging from his position halfway up a lamppost, and waving one arm in the air, was a tall man with dark hair. He was laughing and looked carefree – almost happy.

The camera lingered on him for a brief moment, then moved on.

"Mum," said Jennifer more insistently this time. "Will you buy the paper this week, the one with the special extra pages on the Coronation? I'd like to cut them out for my scrapbook."

Margaret blinked herself back to the present. Had it really been Graham? The camera shot had been so fleeting. How could she be sure?

"Yes, of course I will, love," she managed to say eventually. "It's a special occasion, after all."

She watched in a trance as the celebratory processions were filmed and replayed. The marching troops, the

A WORD FROM THE AUTHOR

"Grainy Coronation footage was showing. A man had climbed a lamppost for a better view. I started to wonder about his family. A story was born."

ILLUSTRATIONS: JOHN HANCOCK, MANDY MURRAY

Caught In The Act

Who will triumph – the kindly would-be writer or the wily, scheming tutor? Enjoy this clever story

By Melanie Keast

Enid, retired dinner lady, wannabe author and altogether nice person (aged seventy-one but not counting), walked over to her seat at the front of the class and sat down. The nine other chairs were still empty, but that was because she always liked to be early for the creative writing class and was usually the first to arrive.

She took her pens and notepad out in readiness and reflected, not for the first time, that if anyone in the class realised how bad her eyesight and hearing were they'd wonder why on earth she bothered to come at all. But Enid was passionate about her writing. She'd heard that Carl Frazer was a difficult man to please and an even harder one to like, but she'd decided that was exactly what she needed. A critic who wasn't afraid to tell it like it was – unlike friends and family who were scared to hurt her feelings.

She put her glasses on and sighed. It really was time to invest in some new specs; trying to see any further than her notebook was like peering through a steamed-up window. She tutted to herself and let them dangle from the chain around her neck while she

switched off her hearing aid, something else that needed renewing. It had been playing up for weeks now, but she generally got the gist of what Mr Frazer said with the help of some of the others after the class. She made a note in her book to remind herself.

Carl Frazer, creative writing teacher, plagiarist and liar arrived five minutes late for the lesson and nodded a curt hello before sitting down opposite Enid. He sensed her eyes upon him immediately but carefully avoided her faded blue gaze, concentrating instead on the other nine people. He wasn't sure, but he had a nagging feeling that the old trout knew what he was up to – had guessed his little scam.

However, he knew she'd give him an opening soon and then he could do a hatchet job on her. Bile was his speciality, and these fledglings usually had fragile egos. Shame, though; of all of them, her work was probably the best. He leafed through the pile of stories as he took

Enid loved the writing classes

From the start, the dignified lady with her steady gaze had disconcerted him

them out of his bag and couldn't suppress a sly grin. This raw talent was producing more than he could have hoped for. He had three excellent ideas for his present book, and loads more for the next. Enid had come up with a cracking plot in the crime scenario he'd set them as homework which he'd liked to have used straight away, but…

He glanced across at her and saw that she was still looking his way. It was her steady gaze that he found so disconcerting; that unreadable expression of hers. He'd tried smiling, but she didn't respond at all. *Silly old bat*, he thought dismissively, but she was definitely beginning to get to him. Ever since the start of this course she'd made him feel uncomfortable. Maybe he was **Continued overleaf…**

just being paranoid? He shrugged and looked away.

Feeling irritated, he set a short piece to write and relaxed while he watched his pupils creating for him. He grazed on their little grey cells with impunity; what they wrote was new, fresh and devoid of copyrights; green and rough around the edges, certainly, but easily re-mouldable in his next book. Only their word against his, if they should ever see their ideas published. Difficult to prove.

Dishonest, certainly, but as he wasn't operating under his real name, they were unlikely to connect the two. Sweet.

His eyes flickered to Enid again, sitting quietly, staring his way, that enigmatic expression cloaking her thoughts. He shivered and took a deep breath; he really did need to get a grip.

Gathering their manuscripts together, he stood up with a scrape of his chair. The class knew what was coming; he could feel the waves of apprehension rolling towards him like mist across a valley. He'd only taught one other creative writing class so far, but in a manifestation of reverse psychology, he'd found that the more he told them they'd never make writers, the harder they seemed to try. He loved it – and the results paid him dividends.

"First I'll return your homework, then we'll listen to some of you read out your latest efforts." He looked at the man by the door. "John: very predictable, almost mundane." He passed the manuscript into the unfortunate John's hand.

"Annette." Annette drew an audible, shuddering breath and held it until he reached her. "Unimaginative." His voice was cool. "And this one, Susan, was dire." He waved the offending short story in the air while Susan blushed. Out of the corner of his eye, Frazer saw Enid shake her head, saw the glasses hanging on a gold chain around her neck glint in the afternoon sunshine.

He doled out the remaining stories, including hers, without another word and strode back to the head of the table feeling rattled. As he sat down, Enid's head bent over her notepad.

The old biddy was always either staring at him or scribbling in her notebook. What was she jotting down now? He cleared his throat noisily to get everyone's attention.

"Have you forgotten what you're here for?" he demanded. "This is a creative writing class. Do you think my novel would have been published if I'd trotted out this garbage, these well-worn plots?" He contemptuously stabbed the air and enjoyed their discomfort. But he let the silence stretch for a beat too long.

"I've read your book, Mr Frazer."

The classes were a perfect cover for his scam

Enid's voice was loud in the hush of the room. "*Poison Petals*. How did you think up such an idea?"

Mmmm… His cold eyes contemplated her for a second. Did she know? Was she telling him that she was onto him? For a moment he felt a feather's touch of fear, and decided he needed time to think.

me. Isn't there anything in my short story that you liked?"

Frazer stared at her lined face with ill-concealed relief. As he'd anticipated – here was his opening, his opportunity to get rid of her.

"Not much," he said rudely. "And to be brutally frank, Enid, now that we're on

"I think you're wasting your time and mine. You're just not good enough"

"Okay, let's take a break," he said, ignoring her question. "Ten minutes."

Surprised but grateful for the change of plan, everyone shifted to the back of the room where the tea and coffee-making facilities were stacked. Frazer remained where he was, deep in thought.

His first crime novel had received excellent reviews and from that he'd been offered a very lucrative two-book deal. Before writing it, he'd been working as an English teacher and the plot had been filched entirely from Keith Harrow, one of his sixth form pupils.

When Keith left school to work abroad, Frazer decided to retire and devote all his time to turning Keith's idea into a best-seller, which he'd done very successfully.

All was well until Frazer came to pen the follow-up. He discovered he had no original ideas; enough writing ability, but not one jot of imagination. That was when he thought up this little scam; one creative writing class a week, two hours of teaching followed by a rewarding harvest of his pupils' ideas.

Easy. Or it had been…

He didn't hear her approach.

"Mr Frazer."

He looked up. Enid was holding up her returned homework. "Mr Frazer – excuse

the subject, I think you're wasting your time and mine by being here. You're just not good enough." He kept his voice low so the rest of the group were unaware of the verbal savaging he was delivering.

Enid's expression remained impassive but she put on her glasses and leaned closer to his table.

Frazer was amazed by her lack of reaction. It ignited his anger, fuelled by the fear that she might be onto him.

"Don't you ever show emotion, Enid? You're like an ageing Mona Lisa. Do you know what they call her inscrutable expression?" His voice was so sharp, it could have drawn blood. "The Gioconda Smile. It's unreadable. Deadpan!"

He was fired up and would have continued if Susan hadn't arrived with a coffee and raised eyebrows. Enid walked away, and Frazer hoped he'd been cruel enough. Surely she wouldn't want to come back. He pretended to sip his drink, watching her in his peripheral vision. She wrote something on her notepad before making her way slowly out to the toilets.

He frowned, exasperated. What had she written now? Curiosity burned so fiercely that he walked quickly over and looked at her open pad.

Continued overleaf…

The words written in Enid's neat hand chilled him. He ran his eyes swiftly down the page that started with his name in capital letters. *CARL FRAZER. Crime. Phone Keith. Sort out hearing. Words and whole sentences missing. Gioconda. Plagiarism. Check with solicitor.*

Frazer broke out in a cold sweat. Damn it – she knew! He hurried to the gents' and locked the door, trying to get his thudding heart under control. What to do? He ran his hands over his face and closed his eyes. Should he tough it out and deny everything, or pack up and head for pastures new?

Frazer only needed seconds to decide; he was a coward as well as a thief. He'd feign illness and leave at once; he could be miles away by the morning. He'd have to ditch the ideas he'd stolen from this lot though; he couldn't use them now.

Good job she wrote things down, too; it wasn't just her ears that weren't working as well as they used to. She printed the name of the new teacher and, underneath, the name of her grandson, Keith, who'd just got back from a week's holiday. She must remember to ring him. She relaxed, took one last look at Mrs Phillips, then took off her glasses and let them hang around her neck. Without them, everything more than a foot away was a complete blur but Enid enjoyed this self-imposed fog; it allowed her to focus.

Enid loved writing crime fiction and had just finished writing her first book. She'd been going to ask Mr Frazer to take a look at it but now that was impossible. Still, maybe she could dedicate it to him because he'd inadvertently given her the inspiration for the title. It was the only

He broke out in a cold sweat and hurried off to the gents'. Damn it, she knew!

Enid sat in her usual place the following Tuesday, surprised by the news. The class had just been informed that Mr Frazer had left and this new person was taking over.

She felt sad. She thought Mr Frazer had been an excellent teacher, a little sharp maybe, but she understood that that was just his way of spurring you on. He'd been published, too, written that marvellous book. Why, she'd even told him so – but he'd been too modest to say anything about it.

Enid sighed and listened to Mrs Phillips, the new tutor. She adjusted her new hearing aid and congratulated herself on finally getting round to doing something about her increasing deafness.

words she'd heard when she'd spoken to him last time. *A Gioconda Smile*, he'd said. It had struck her straight away as a terrific title; her only doubt being that it wasn't her idea, so she'd checked it wasn't plagiarism with the solicitor who lived next door before using it.

Enid sighed. She was sure Mr Frazer would have been so interested to hear all about it.

A WORD FROM THE AUTHOR
I attend a creative writing class to 'grease the wheels' and this plot came to me while I was watching my eagle-eyed tutor.

Teatime Treat

Mini Tarts

WITH CLOTTED CREAM

Ingredients

- 1x350g (12oz) shortcrust pastry
- 180g (6oz) caster sugar
- 3 eggs
- 175ml (6fl oz) double cream
- 125ml (4fl oz) lemon juice
- 1tsp grated lemon rind

To serve:
Clotted cream, berries (eg raspberries, blueberries) and a dusting of icing sugar

JUICY FRUIT TOPPING

Preparation time: 10mins
Cooking time: 29mins
Makes 12 tarts

● Preheat the oven to 200°C, Fan Oven 180°C, Gas Mark 6. Roll out the **pastry** to 2mm (⅛in) thick, prick and cut into circles to fit muffin tins. Place into muffin tins, line with non-stick baking paper and fill with **baking beans**. Bake for 5mins, remove the beans and return to the oven for 5mins, or until the pastry is light golden. Remove from the oven and allow to cool.

● Reduce the oven temp to 160°C, Fan Oven 150°C, Gas Mark 2.

● Place the **sugar**, **eggs**, **cream**, **lemon juice** and **rind** in a jug and mix. Pour into the **tart shells** and bake for 20mins or until the filling is just set.

● Cool, top with **clotted cream** and **berries** and dust with **icing sugar**.

RECIPES/STYLING: ANNE LOWE PHOTOGRAPHY: UPFRONT PHOTOGRAPHY

A Letter From

**When Jean received a letter addressed to her late husband,
little did she know how its contents would touch their lives**

By Jenny Wyper

s Lucy waited impatiently by the garden gate for their expected taxi, Jean's two older daughters sat with her at the kitchen table, alternately holding her hand or topping up her tea, seeking reassurance that their mother was certain she was doing the right thing.

And she was, she assured them – at least now that she had time to get her head round it, although she hadn't known quite what to do when the letter first arrived.

Heart and mind had run the full gauntlet of emotions and she was glad she was sitting down when she opened it, otherwise she would have collapsed on the kitchen floor.

years, the letter also informed her that the author was visiting the UK the following month on business and was keen to get in touch.

The signature, Stephen Plonk, meant nothing at all to Jean and the fact that her late husband may have had other relationships before meeting her, meant even less; what had gone before had never been an issue for either of them.

But the fact that her husband may have had a child before starting a family with her, and never even mentioned it, was a completely different matter altogether.

Jean's first thought, once she had gathered her wits about her, was whether to tell her three girls. So to begin with she confided only in her middle daughter Carol, the most level-headed of the three.

"I have discovered that you, Robert Service, are my father" the letter revealed

The correspondence from America was addressed to her late husband, Bob, and was curiously formal considering the startling information it relayed, stating quite simply –

Sir, My mother Margaret Plonk sadly passed away recently and on attending to her personal effects I have discovered that you, Robert Service, are my father.

If that in itself wasn't enough to knock the stuffing out of any woman, happily married until recently for twenty-five

Carol's counsel was that her mother should at least call this chap Plonk and check his claim, reasoning that if he was their father's child from an earlier relationship, then he was surely entitled to know his father had died.

Jean wasn't looking forward to relaying that particular information but checking from his letter where he would be staying during his visit, Jean called his hotel the day before he was due to arrive and left her name and phone number at the

America

She hadn't known what to do when the letter first arrived

extreme in that gushing way Americans can be, totally overwhelming Jean with his delight and gratitude for getting in touch.

But when he went off at full tilt, firing question after question at her, she stopped him in his tracks. Jean had questions of her own that she needed answers to.

After having apologised for his directness, Stephen told Jean that until his mother's recent death, all he knew about his father was his name; Robert Service.

Apparently his mother had fallen pregnant with him shortly before she and Bob had decided to go their separate ways, he moving back to Scotland. She had kept the pregnancy secret, her reasoning being that despite their

reception for Mr Plonk to pick up.

The extra day was to give her time to prepare herself. But to her surprise, Mr Plonk called back almost immediately.

Initially he was garrulous in the

relationship having come to a natural end, Robert would never have left her had he known about the baby. That was the kind of man he was, Stephen's **Continued overleaf…**

mother had told him; decent, loving and caring.

Jean was touched by the young American's obvious sincerity and felt a tear fall from her eye as she listened to his story. It was undoubtedly true that the Bob she knew and loved would never have abandoned his child if he had known of the situation, and when she heard this young American describe a man he had never even met with such obvious longing, she realised there and then he couldn't be anyone other than Robert's long-lost son.

But that meant having to tell him that his father had died before he even had a chance to meet him.

It was almost like having to tell her daughters all over again.

The hotel was truly opulent

"Personally I think you've lost your marbles," Jean's oldest daughter Jilly told her. "He's probably a conman who preys on the recently bereaved."

"Oh, don't talk such rot, Jilly!" Carol reprimanded her sister. "Dad would need to have known about him before leaving him anything, and it's patently obvious he didn't," she added.

"You don't know that," Jilly answered. "Maybe it was to be his dark secret until after he'd died."

"Don't you even suggest such a thing," Jean snapped. "If your father had known about a child of his, he would have shared that knowledge with me before we were married."

Jilly, a "resting" actress, put on her wounded prima donna face. Well used to her theatrics, Jean ignored her and rose to clear the breakfast dishes. Before she reached the sink however, one of Lucy's piercing teenage screams rent the air and both mother and older daughters rushed outside to check on the commotion.

"Look!" Lucy shrieked as her mother and siblings stumbled out on to the driveway. "It's our taxi!"

"If that's a taxi it's the biggest taxi I've ever seen," her mother remarked.

"It… it's a stretch limo," Jilly said, stammering her lines with excitement. "As used by Prime Ministers and rich Arab Princes."

"Or successful conmen," Carol suggested, sarcastically.

Even when her husband Bob was alive, Jean had never been inside an edifice that screamed pure opulence the way this amazing hotel did.

As she stepped inside, her mind boggled at the thought of what it must cost just to spend one night there, let alone a whole month. Despite the credit crunch however, cost obviously meant nothing to the hotel's affluent clientele for the reception area was bustling with guests. Jean was beginning to feel decidedly out of place in the High Street suit she had, up until then, felt like a million dollars in.

"Goodness! It's a celeb spotter's paradise," Carol remarked, as they took a seat while reception rang Mr Plonk's

home," Jean asked, unimpressed.

"Only the hottest ticket in Hollywood!" Carol exclaimed.

Jean watched Hollywood's Royal Family look round reception, searching for someone. Then the boy caught her eye and broke into a child's knowing smile.

"Tell me, Jilly," Jean asked her actress

"He still has to prove his credentials before he can be a member of this family"

room to announce their arrival. "I've seen a minor Royal, three Members of Parliament and one elderly pop star – and that's just in reception."

"I'd love Stephen to be a pop star," Lucy said earnestly. "Can you imagine what my school friends would say?"

"Let's not get carried away with ourselves," Jilly said, affectedly. "He still has to prove his credentials before he can be a member of this family."

Having spoken to him on the phone several times now, Jean no longer had any doubts about Stephen's credentials but she prayed that he would resemble her late husband in some physical way, just to put her daughters' minds at ease.

When her wish was granted, it didn't happened quite as she had expected.

"Goodness!" Carol exclaimed in an urgent whisper. "Is that who I think it is?"

Jean and her other two daughters followed Carol's direction to see a tall, strikingly handsome young black man exiting the lift with a stunning blonde on his arm and in between them, the cutest three-year-old child Jean had ever seen.

"Oh my God!" Jilly shrieked. "That… that's Steve Newman and Angelika Lindstrom and their son!"

"And who are they when they're at

daughter. "If your family name was Plonk, would your agent make you change it?"

"In a heartbeat," Jilly replied.

"To something like Newman, perhaps?"

All three of Jean's daughters stared at her, momentarily puzzled, then Jilly's jaw dropped open.

"You… you can't possibly mean…!"

Before Jean could answer, the cutest child she had ever seen came running across the foyer and skidded to a halt before their table. He was lighter skinned than his father, but had his big brown eyes and mother's wide mouth – but his most prominent feature was his grandfather Bob's button nose.

"Hi!" he said, removing his baseball cap and pushing his fingers through his thick black hair. "Are you guys my Scottish family?"

A WORD FROM THE AUTHOR

"Genealogy has always fascinated me. After all, who knows who our forbears were, or how wonderfully culturally diverse our descendants yet to come will be."

ILLUSTRATIONS: ISTOCKPHOTO, INGLIS THORBURN

Over The Fence

Sometimes it takes an offended grandchild and a cheeky squirrel to overcome the reserve of two lonely people…

By Beth James

"Grandma, why's that old man next door so grumpy?" Jeanette straightened up from where she'd been weeding and cutting back in her bed of perennials. With the back of a muddy hand, she absently pushed a lock of grey-brown hair from her eyes. "Grumpy? What makes you think he's grumpy?"

"Well, he never smiles, and he's got this massive water pistol he fires at squirrels. I think that's cruel – really cruel."

Looking at her granddaughter's vehement face, Jeanette could not resist a smile. "I bet he never catches them," she said. "They're too smart, and anyway he's only trying to frighten them.

"He's got a soft heart really, you know. He puts out food for the birds and doesn't want the squirrels pinching it before the blue tits get a look-in."

By this time, Maisie, her face screwed up with concentration, was busily balancing on Jeanette's hosepipe, tightrope fashion. "Well, I think he's grumpy anyway. He looks at the squirrels as though he really hates them – and he never smiles at me."

"I won't be smiling at you if you split that hosepipe. Off you get, madam! It's time for you to wash your hands and face before Mum collects you."

Maisie scowled. "Why do I have to always wash before Mum gets here, when I've been dirty all day?"

"Just do it," said Jeanette.

At the other side of the fence Norman was fixing some of the wayward rambling rose's new growth to the wires carefully put up on his side of the fence. Hmm! A grumpy old man, was he? Strangely, he found he objected to the "old" rather more than the "grumpy". Sixty-eight wasn't so old, was it?

Norman glowered before tying in a particularly vicious length of thorny stem. "That should fix you – you little blighters," he said to any squirrel that just happened to be within earshot.

A grumpy old man, was he? Actually he objected to "old" more than "grumpy"

want the squirrels pinching it before the blue tits get a look-in."

So the new lady next door thought his war with the squirrels was simply a matter of blue tit protection, did she? Hmm, well, he'd have to think about that one. True, he did feed the birds. Watching the birds feed was something to do in the long winter months as he ate his lonely breakfast. Besides, Sue had always fed the birds, and somehow he'd carried it on **Continued overleaf…**

**Jeanette could not
resist a smile**

just in case she was up there, perched on a cloud somewhere, watching what he was doing.

Not that he believed in any of that nonsense, of course. When you were dead, you were dead. That was all there was to it. But, well, life had to go on – even for the blue tits.

A squirrel ran nimbly along the top of the wooden panelled fence, a walnut in his mouth. He sprang into the branches of Jeanette's plum tree and sat making cracking noises with the nut. Then he shimmied his beautiful tail, tossed the nutshells over the fence, and – Norman was certain – grinned at him.

"I'll get you, you varmint," muttered Norman reaching for his garishly coloured water gun. "You won't be burying any more nuts in my winter pansy pots."

The pansy pots had also become something that Norman felt he ought to do. "I love their dear little faces," Sue used to say. "They're so cheerful. So forgiving. I defy anyone to feel miserable when they're in flower."

Norman aimed the gun, but the jet of water missed the squirrel, which, barely pausing to chuckle over his shoulder, scampered on his way.

There was a strangled screech from the other side of the fence.

"Well! Thanks a lot!"

Jeanette's face surrounded by her dripping hair peered over the top of the fence. Norman went hot and cold, then hot again. In spite of being grumpy, he hadn't failed to notice that Jeanette was an extremely attractive woman. A bit of all right she would have been described as in his day. But Norman well knew his day had long since gone. Or had it?

"I'm s-so sorry," he stammered. "I was aiming at the squirrel, not you... I – I thought you'd gone indoors with your granddaughter."

Jeanette's outraged expression started to soften. "Well, as you can see, I hadn't! I'm still here and I'm wet!"

"I'm sorry," murmured Norman again, watching fascinated as Jeanette's curvy mouth began to form a smile. "If only I could make it up to you," he continued recklessly. "Tell me – do you like pansies?" *What a stupid question,* he thought immediately. She'd think he was crackers as well as grumpy!

"Well, yes, I love pansies – but it was an accident, wasn't it?" Her smile widened, exposing slightly uneven, but very white, teeth. She turned away, laughing. "I can't take your pansies. A little bit of water never hurt anyone."

"No – really." Norman was suddenly desperate to keep her attention. "I've grown too many. I've been winning the war against the squirrels this year, so I've plenty to spare... Honestly."

What was the matter with him? He was practically pleading! Why did it seem so inordinately important that she should accept his gesture of goodwill?

On her side of the fence Jeanette was struggling with her surprise. When Norman smiled his whole face lit up, making him not unattractive. She knew

"I'm s-so sorry," he stammered. "I was aiming at the squirrel – not at you"

"I'll only accept if you'll come over and share a pot of tea with me"

from Gabby, three doors down, that Norman's wife Sue, had died three years before and he'd had to fight to come to terms with his loss. Well, she knew how that felt, and that was why she'd done little more than nod at him in the six months since she'd moved next door. And now here he was, this sunny Saturday afternoon, being almost human.

"Ah – this war you have with the squirrels," she started.

Norman held up a protesting hand. "Oh, I know," he said. "You think it's cruel. It's just a deterrent – that's all. It's not intended to harm them. This time of year when I'm putting in the winter pansies, they're busy burying their nuts, and the two clash a bit. My pansies tend to get turfed out in the process."

Jeanette smiled. "Oh, I'm not worried." She indicated the branch of the plum tree where the squirrel was sitting preening his tail. "Judging by his expression, he enjoys the game as much as you do. And I will have some of your pansies. They have such lovely little faces, they quite cheer me up in the winter."

Norman gave a lop-sided grin and Jeanette's heart melted. Grumpy old man? Norman? No way.

"But I'll only accept them," she added, "if you'll come over and share a pot of tea with me. Give me half an hour – my daughter and Maisie will be gone by then and I'll be more than ready for a tea break, I can tell you."

This time Norman tried not to let his answering smile split his face in two. Silly old fool that he was. He just nodded and gave a half wave as Jeanette's head disappeared from view.

Then as he started towards the back door, intending to wash and brush up a little bit before venturing next door, a movement in one of the pots by the back steps caught his eye. Automatically, he reached for the squirrel gun. Then he froze, mid-action, and stood watching as the squirrel deftly buried his nut and scampered away by his usual route of the fence and plum tree.

You have to admire them really, thought Norman. Resourceful, friendly little creatures, squirrels – he'd always thought so!

A WORD FROM THE AUTHOR

"Every year the squirrels strip the nuts from our walnut tree, then they turn their attention to my winter pansies. But my husband now has a water gun..."

Wanted On The Voyage

Share the breathless excitement as a secret romance leads Molly to take a leap of faith into a whole new life

By Kate Harrison Whiteside

The London docks beside the Queen Mary are a masterpiece of mayhem. People struggle through the pandemonium, buskers try to outplay each other and vendors try to out-shout each other. Raggedy muffin children peck at pockets like chickens. Trunks and cases are thrown about with complete disregard for contents. I look up the Thames towards the outline of the Parliament buildings, where Father took me once during a land tax protest. But he was not in the crowd.

I look down at the one-way ticket in my hand. All it took was a dare, whispered in my ear at the tennis end-of-season party. Until then, the biggest gamble I had taken was placing secret bets on the horses through our gardener's son. But this time I had staked everything on love.

The ship's horn sounds one frighteningly loud blast and suddenly the melee on shore takes shape. Lines form for the ship's lower decks intake. The misshapen piles of luggage become organised by type, like vegetables at the market. Men appear from nowhere to load trunks, cases and animal cages.

One summer, one whisper, and the one life I know is to change forever.

I remember the day I told Father and Mother. The dankness from the spring draught carried down the chimney on the pigeons' cooing made my nose itch. A damp patch formed just above the waistline of my woollen skirt. The grandfather clock ticked away, distracting me.

I mapped out my speech carefully, each word a set stitch in a tapestry. But, as the minutes passed, they unravelled in my head. Mother supervised Lizzie in the kitchen as she made tea. Father was due to return from a meeting down in London with a client wishing to purchase a well-known Lincolnshire estate. Time ate away at my confidence, like the seeds the birds nibbled in the wooden feeder outside the sitting room window.

This simply was the biggest gamble of my life — I had staked everything on love

I shall never forget the thrill as he whispered to me

I had already written to tell my sister, Dorothy. She had gone to the continent with friends of the family. Her reply had arrived promptly, telling me I had been struck by lightning and Father would be furious. She said she'd pray for me – and if I did not tell her each development as it happened, she'd pray for another bolt of lightning to strike me down. Dear brother John, serving in India, said I was mad, but that a little insanity could be a good **Continued overleaf…**

Continued from previous page

thing. He'd seen it spring up in unlikely places and with surprising results. Though he offered support, he could not guarantee Father's, nor influence him.

John is Father's favourite. He is the family diamond. I, on the other hand, merit only a pearl rating, the kind you get from street vendors in China Town. I was a bit too rough around the edges and needed polishing, I overheard Father describe me to Mother only recently. Why didn't I do something with my life? And, was there to be no sign of a husband for either of his daughters? Well, I was about to open Pandora's box.

I had originally seen him coming in and out of Father's land agency offices, where I worked filing documents on Tuesdays and Thursdays. Everyone was talking about him – the striking apprentice nephew of solicitor Thomas Loy. I had witnessed more than one woman quickly bring a fan to her face to cool a rising blush as he walked by.

The rumours of our relationship began to cause ripples about town shortly after the first cricket match of the season. He had just returned from a series in Argentina with England's team, worthy of a full sports page in the paper. He spent a lot of time after the match talking to my father about business.

We were formally introduced by his uncle, Mr Loy, at the first tennis tournament of the season at Sutton on Sea. His handshake lasted an unsociably long time; it wasn't the first time we had held hands.

We met again at rehearsals for the summer solstice theatre production of *Romeo and Juliet* by Alford's Shakespeare Club. He played Romeo. At the last minute I was called on to fill in for

What lay across the ocean?

Juliet, as the leading lady had taken ill. The play fired up even more rumblings.

Then, we ended up partners for the doubles finals. But this was not the only time we'd been together over the summer; just the first time we'd been seen out in public.

As he held our winners' trophy in front of his face, he whispered to me.

"Meet me at the back of the club after the photographs are taken. I have something important to put to you."

He winked and the trophy was returned to the table.

The photographs took forever. Longer than it is taking for this ship to set sail. I remember the feeling I had, the moment he whispered in my ear, his rough skin brushing my cheek. I had never been so certain of a decision in my life.

"Only if we keep it a secret," I replied.

And so began the waiting for the right time to tell Father and Mother.

We acted out our own secret play for what seemed an eternity. My hours were filled with writing the history column for the Alford Gazetteer, exhibiting my paintings, and filing at Father's offices. I pretended to be shocked when Robin's leaving was formally announced.

While everyone was distracted preparing for his bon voyage party, we rode our bicycles separately out to the beach. My heart beat faster than the pedals would go round. Past the windmill. Past Grange Green. Past the Hare and Hound pub. After checking that no one saw us, we walked down the beach around the first bend. The sand dunes became our sitting room. He sat facing the sun, whilst I kept my back to it, an umbrella to hand. We discussed our plans. I used my hands to make a frame and in my mind painted Robin's long body, black, wavy hair blown this way and that, and memorised every feature.

runs my mother's family business – Lamb's Navy Rum – in the city. It is usually just Uncle when I visit. Aunty Flo spends most of her time studying piano with Lechetiski in Paris.

We took in Harold Brighouse's *Hobson's Choice* at the Apollo, dined on oysters at The Savoy. Uncle was the first person I told face-to-face about my clandestine plan. It was met with a bottle of champagne, a gallant speech and crystal flute toasts.

"Ah, Molly, following in your brother's footsteps. Your mother will miss you, but support you. I will make sure my sister stands by you. Just go – new frontiers beckon. But your father, there is a challenge. You are at risk of cutting all ties – and there is a penalty for that. I suspect you will be taken out of the will."

We weaved our way home across Regent's Park, arm in arm, sitting on every bench we passed and adding to the list of things I must pack.

"Worry not, darling niece. I shall make sure you are kept in the style to which

"Worry not, darling niece. We must stick together, we who don't quite fit in"

Throwing his head back, laughing, his last words to me were, "I can't believe you are honouring my dare, Molly Higgins."

Dramatics lessons proved to be worth their weight in gold. I smiled and went about my life as if nothing had changed. This surprised the gossips, as Robin left Alford a day after the grand farewell party at the Conservative Club, which I did not attend.

Instead I travelled down to London to see Uncle Charles, Mother's youngest brother, who always spoilt me. Charles

you're accustomed. We must stick together, we who don't quite fit in."

Alford became unbearably empty after Robin left. Eyebrows continued to go up and down and lips moved behind gloved hands. But, the dare was on, and I kept my promise. A secret it would remain.

The ship's horn sounded twice. I jumped, as I had when Father had slammed the front door, announcing his arrival home. Lizzie brought in tea and **Continued overleaf…**

Continued from previous page

winked at me as she backed out of the room. I so desired a deep breath, but the ties at the back of my dress forbade it.

I rose as Father entered the room. He stood behind the armchair Mother sat in, looking at me with a quizzical look.

"Well, Molly. You have something to say to us, I believe."

A small moan came from Mother. She peeked up at me over her fan, not daring to look back at Father.

"You'll see to her packing. I do wish been putting china and linens in a trunk for you in the upstairs sitting room for some time now. I shall do a listing and see what else you need. But I cannot come to London with you. I cannot bear to say goodbye."

Father shook my hand the night before I left Alford, as he was off to Scotland at first light. When I awoke there was an envelope on my night table, his business seal on it. Inside were a large sum of notes and three bonds. On the outside was Mother's handwriting.

"We can be married in Montreal, the moment you arrive," he had whispered

you well, Molly. But you know that once you leave, it is unlikely you shall return. Just go. I will not have my family disgraced any further."

When Father left, Mother rushed over and clasped me in her arms.

"Molly, what shall you do? Where shall you live? I *suspected* you were up to something. You seemed, for once, to have a focus. Perhaps you will find this new life more suitable to your independent ways.

"We are a generation apart, you and I. My path is laid out; I simply must follow it. Yours is uncharted. I am a little jealous.

"But you shall have to go through Uncle Charles if you need anything. I am not strong enough to change your father's mind on anything. Only strong enough to live with it. He means well. You must forgive him."

"Thank you, Mother. I am fine. I have known about this for months, and been preparing myself. Robin is there now, and has a home for us. He shall meet me when the ship docks."

"We do not have much time. I have

The ship's horn blasted three long wails, signalling our departure. As the waves whispered around the bow, and London faded behind me, I remembered the feeling of Robin's stubbly face against my cheek and the words that would change my life forever.

"Molly, I dare you to come to Canada. I will be leaving with my family in September; you can come in the spring. We can be married in Montreal, the moment you arrive. Let me know when your ship is to dock."

As she moves slowly out to sea, I whisper into the wind.

"I'll be arriving in Montreal on the first of May, Robin."

But he already knows that.

A WORD FROM THE AUTHOR

"My English grandparents migrated to Canada in the early 1900s under a cloud. I snooped, but their secrets remain buried."

Fancy That!

Fabulous 50s facts to make you go "Wow!"

Only a little bit!

Fast Woman

High flying

Jacqueline Cochran became the first woman to break the sound barrier, piloting an F-86 Sabre, in 1953

Fact!
Petrol rationing was introduced between December 1956 and April 1957 because of the Suez crisis

WOW! ⬤ **50s invention Velcro gets its name from the French words velours (velvet) and crochet (hook).**

⬤ The first Polio vaccine was developed in 1952 by Jonas Salk.

⬤ **Sweet rationing was lifted in 1953.**

⬤ Camay soap was launched in 1958 with the TV jingle, "You'll be a little lovelier each day."

⬤ **The modern seat-belt was invented by Swedish engineer Nils Bohlin and fitted in a 1959 Volvo.**

⬤ **Lego gets its name from the Danish words led godt, meaning play well.**

⬤ 1950 saw the TV debuts of Watch With Mother and Andy Pandy.

WOW! ⬤ **Christopher Cockerell's invention the hovercraft took to the sea in 1959.**

⬤ The atomic clock was invented by Jack Parry and Louis Essen in 1955.

⬤ **Birds Eye frozen fish fingers were introduced to Britain in 1955, although only 30% of homes had a refrigerator.**

Feeling On Top Of The World

Reach for the sky

Nepalese Sherpa Tenzing Norgay and mountaineer Edmund Hillary were the first people to reach the top of Mount Everest in 1953

A Class Of My Own

Be yourself, her sister told her. But she wouldn't meet the man of her dreams in a cake decorating class, would she?

By Lydia Jones

Just enjoy being single." My sister waves immaculately French manicured fingers across her cappuccino. "All that time to please yourself."

She closes eyes in mock ecstasy and sucks froth from her spoon. "When the right bloke comes along, you won't have any of that any more."

"As if," I say despondently.

"Seriously, Rach – it'll happen. One stomach-swirlingly delicious moment and you'll just know."

"Oh, Pen – you're such a romantic. I'm afraid I don't wear the same rose-tinted specs as you do."

"Please don't tell me you're actually letting that utter berk Jake's betrayal

photocopier are Old Man Flintoff's asking for month-end figures." I groan, then add, "But, trust me, because I have a cunning plan."

Her eyes widen. "Not online dating?"

"No! I'm nowhere near brave enough. But I've decided… if this were any other area of my life, I wouldn't just be sitting round waiting for something to happen. I mean, I'm usually pretty organised, right?"

She nods. "No one to touch you."

"So instead of waiting for Fate to bring me my perfect man, I'm going to go out and find him."

"Don't do anything drastic, Rach."

I wave away her anxiety with enthusiasm. "You're always telling me to get out more – and right now, Friday night supermarket shopping with you is the only social highlight of my life."

I'm going to enrol in the classes that have the best-looking blokes in them

make you all bitter and twisted?"

"Absolutely not. I just think sometimes romance might need a helping hand."

"What about work?" she asks.

I wrinkle my nose. "Trust me, the only eyes likely to meet mine across the

"Yes, but –" she says rather warily.

"So –" I brandish the prospectus from my bag. "The college are running taster sessions where you get to try out as many evening classes as you like for free. I'm going to enrol for lots of classes and sign

**I wanted to make
my niece's birthday
cake really special**

up for the ones with the best-looking single blokes on them!"

"Not a disastrous plan." She purses lips thoughtfully. "But it'd be a whole lot better if you just took the classes that interested *you*. Just be yourself."

"Do you have any idea how much you just sounded like the solution from a magazine problem page?"

She giggles and shrugs simultaneously.

"I'll take that as a compliment, then?"

"*Be true to yourself.*" My hands make speech marks in the air. "*And all will turn out well, my dear.*"

"Maybe you should listen to the experts."

"Whatever."

She gathers up her bags and car keys and says regretfully, "Got to run."

"Go on." I kiss her Chanel-scented **Continued overleaf…**

cheek. "Get your smug-married self out of here and let me sip my solitary coffee in peace. I'm sticking with my plan."

"Okay. Just don't sign up for car maintenance, whatever you do – it's bound to be full of hysterical spinsters seeking someone to hold their spanners."

I love my sister to bits, but she doesn't understand that not everyone is lucky enough to meet the man of their dreams on the first day of a new job, like she did.

And "being yourself" is all very well if you're an even-post-baby perfect size ten, like Penny. I'm a bit more on the buxom side myself. Besides, I don't know many men who are into EastEnders, Jackie Collins and cake decorating.

You were right about car maintenance," I tell her the following Friday. "I sat next to a sparky woman called Hilary who had a PhD in bio-chemistry, but chewed my ear off all evening about how hard it is to meet suitable men – I mean, she's telling me?"

"What about the other classes?"

I tick them off on my fingers. "Tai-chi; full of adolescents – quite muscular, mind you, some of them. But I'm not into being the older woman mother-figure. Local

Her eyes sparkle and I find my mouth smiling. "Kind of like Phil Mitchell, but a lot cuter. Sort of solid and sweet."

"And you spoke to him?"

"No – he was reeling off a long list of ingredients."

She sighs in sympathy. "Which his wife probably gave him."

"Exactly. By the way, I thought I'd make Molly's cake really girly; all pink bows and flowers and stuff."

"Sounds great. It's really sweet of you to do the cake for her, Rach."

"My pleasure. She is my goddaughter as well as my niece, after all. Anyway you know I love posh cake decorating."

"But where to now with the finding-the-perfect-man plan?"

"Actually, one good thing did come out of car maintenance. The teacher offered to take a group of us to a car rally at the weekend – you never know!"

"Have you gone stark staring mad?" Penny clatters her cup for emphasis. "Earth to Planet Rachel. Car rally? That means mud and wind, hanging about for hours in the freezing cold waiting for the occasional car to flash past. Where's the fun in that?"

"I'll let you know once I've been there."

I know it's dead corny but I've never seen a bloke with such lovely blue eyes

history; nice lot, but all a bit brainy for me. Digital photography; friendly bunch, fun to be with. A few single men, too."

"Sounds promising – nice single men?"

"Very nice. And not one of them a day under seventy. The only good-looking bloke I've spotted all week was in the confectionery shop next door."

"What was he like? Do tell."

I cross fingers behind my back. One of the things I really can't abide about my big sister is that she is nearly always right.

The next week I moan over consoling double-choc mocha to Penny. "I should have known what kind of day it would be when the teacher told us all to pack our own toilet rolls."

My sister is always right

"Too much information." Penny holds up a halt-sign hand. "Please don't go into details. So what's this week's plan then?"

I shrug. "I've had it with the bloke hunting bit for now. But I signed up for cake decorating – thought I might get some ideas for Molly's birthday cake."

"Good idea." She smiles approvingly.

But when I get there I find I am actually a middle-aged woman in the body of a twenty-five-year-old. I'm in cake decorating class and there isn't a person here who looks like she couldn't draw a pension soon. And no men. So what? – at least it's a class I know I'll enjoy.

The door opens.

"Good evening, ladies."

Okay, now I know I've fallen into an alternative universe where coincidences like this actually happen: our teacher is the cuter-than-Phil Mitchell guy from the confectioner's. He smiles at the class and when his gaze reaches me he does a double-take. Or am I seeing things?

He makes the demonstration simple in no-fuss Jamie Oliver fashion and soon has us all hanging on his every word.

"Here's what you'll need for next week," he says, handing out a printed list of ingredients.

"You were in the confectioner's, last week, weren't you?" He hovers over my table. "I noticed you come in."

Definitely defective hearing now too. Did he just say he noticed me?

"Yeah... I... em, was looking for stuff for my niece's cake." My throat is as dry as a flour-dusted baking tin. "She's three next month and I wanted to do something special and girly for her."

He waves a broad finger in the air and mock-frowns as if deep in thought. "I remember you bought nasty pre-made pink sugar bows."

I wince. "Guilty."

He grins and I feel like I'm bathing in the warmth of it.

"I remember thinking, *I wish she'd come to my class. I could teach her how to make her own.* And here you are."

His eyes are twinkling and I know I should be thinking it's dead corny but all I know is my stomach is swirling faster than butter-cream frosting and I've never seen a bloke with such blue eyes.

"Thanks," I say and put out my hand for the ingredient list.

He looks down and laughs like he's forgotten all about it. "See you next week, then," he says and grins again.

"It's a date," I say and grin back.

A WORD FROM THE AUTHOR

"I think we all worry far too much about how people see us when all we need to do is be ourselves. If others don't like it – tough!"

Red Roses For My Love

Rich, dark red and velvety, the bouquet of roses meant so much. But I could hardly bear to look at them, sitting alone

By Celia K Andrew

he roses were the colour of fresh blood. I felt sick at the sight of them, but I smiled and thanked Mr Lambert for his kindness. It must have taken a lot for him to bring them across at this time.

"I hope you don't mind," he told me sadly. "They came today – I forgot I'd ordered them for our anniversary. I don't want them to go to waste, though, and but had nothing else to show for their careful breeding.

Our new neighbour, Cecily Lambert, had fallen and broken her hip and had been transferred to the nearest big District General, 40 miles away, for a hip replacement operation. Her husband was closing up the house and moving in with their daughter, to be nearer to the hospital. Nobody knew how long they would be away.

I put the flowers in water. It felt wrong,

Beautiful to look at, I lifted the bouquet to my face but the roses had no scent

they'll only die in the house, what with me going away as well."

His Adam's apple bobbed as he spoke, then he turned away abruptly, raising a hand in mute farewell. I watched him shuffle over the road back to Number Eight and let himself in through his front door. He closed it quietly, without looking at me again.

I lifted the bouquet to my face, but there was no scent. The two dozen velvety roses were beautiful to look at and had probably cost a small fortune,

somehow, having them on display in the front room, so I took them upstairs to my husband's study and set them down in front of the blank computer screen.

They looked as though they were in front of a shrine. I hastily moved them across to the corner cabinet instead. Poor unwanted flowers. The poor Lamberts.

I went back down to the kitchen and threw away the cellophane wrapper, then wondered what to do for supper.

The front door banged. "Hi, Alison," I
Continued overleaf…

Rich and velvety —
but unwanted

called. "How was school today, then?"

"Not chosen for the under-fifteens netball team. Not chosen for the under-fifteens swimming team."

My daughter's feet stamped up the stairs and her bedroom door slammed as well. No doubt her iPod was deafening her, but all I got was silence.

Definitely pizza for supper, then. Alison's favourite, and she most obviously needed cheering up.

read it out. "*C – love you forever – B.* Well? What's this about?"

"Oh, those! They were for –"

"You're having an affair, aren't you? Dad's away for six months, and you've found someone else already!"

"Alison, don't be ridiculous!"

"And you had the nerve to put them in Dad's own study, where you thought nobody would see them!"

"Ali, you've got it all wrong –"

"Who are the roses from, Mum? You're having an affair – how could you?"

The smell of the packet Parmesan made me heave, so I grated cheddar up instead. I made the dough for the base and chopped up salad, listening to the wonderful Dam Busters March on Classic FM.

"You're truly despicable! I'm going to Fiona's." She ripped the gold-edged card in half, flung the pieces to the floor and flounced out.

Oh, my God, she really believes it! I plunged my arms into the washing-up basin to clean off the flour and felt the rip of steel on my fingers. The water turned scarlet. I stared at it for a whole second before the pain cut in. The front door banged. I grabbed for a tea-towel. The sight of the blood was too much and I only just got the basin out of the sink in time.

Alison's footsteps creaked across the landing and I knew she was sneaking into her dad's study to use his computer – faster broadband, more memory, better for games. Deaf ear time, I thought. She was having a bad day, was missing her father – weren't we both! – and was probably in hormonal turmoil as well, so best just to let this pass.

I was all but conducting the March when she came stomping angrily back down the stairs. "Who are the roses from, Mum?" Her voice lashed out from the hall doorway. "Who is 'B' and why will he love you forever?"

I stared at her, floury arms raised for the finale of the March. Her face was drawn into a tight-jawed grimace. She held a gold-rimmed card in her hand and

By the time I'd pulled myself together, wrapped my hand up and cleaned the sink, I'd gone off the whole idea of baking anything. I wasn't hungry and clearly Alison wasn't going to be in for supper anyway.

Fourteen-year-olds! She deserved an absolute rollocking for her behaviour – but not this time. She was already upset over her dad and not getting onto the teams; finding that card and the roses had just tipped her over the edge.

Give her a few hours and she'd be back,

I tried to be understanding, I really did

by the time I'd finished and I had to admit defeat and bin it.

Upstairs I found the roses flung all over the study floor, the cream carpet dark with their spilt water.

I gathered up the beautiful blooms – fresh enough not to have come to much harm from their treatment – and found I could not bear to throw them away. Irrationally, I thought that if I did, the hip operation might go wrong and Cecily Lambert might not recover.

I started to cry again as I tied the rose stems together with one of Alison's hair ribbons. I must be pre-menstrual to be so emotional and pathetic over some stupid roses. I carried them to the bathroom, filled their vase again and replaced them in the study.

wanting Rocky Road ice-cream with pistachio nuts. Her dad would have given her such a row for speaking to me like that, but he wasn't here and she was always unutterably awful for a few weeks when he first went away. I was trying to be understanding, I really was, but inside I just felt like crying.

The torn pieces of card, when I had put them together again, spoke of our new neighbours' fifty-year love affair.

Simon and I had made it to sixteen

Alison rang from Fiona's at nine to ask me to collect her. She sounded about ten years old again and very ashamed and upset about what she'd said.

Thank God she's stopped thinking I'm having an affair, I thought as we drove home in silence.

I retrieved the card from the bin and

I started to cry again as I tied the rose stems together with her hair ribbon

years with never a serious row – but an awful lot of miserable partings and then glorious reunions. Army life's like that, but you get used to it.

I ineptly dressed my fingers, then found the sticky tape and stuck the card back together. There was blood all over it

explained about the Lamberts. "Cecily, not Caroline," I said, tracing over the C with my plastered fingers. She burst into tears and I joined in. What a day!

She slept, but I didn't. Indigestion all night long kept me up and half the **Continued overleaf…**

cupboards in the house were cleared out by morning. My fingers kept breaking out bloody again and I went to the doctor after Alison had left for school.

He finished bandaging up my fingers completely flabbergasted. "Oh, Caroline, I'm so sorry," he said earnestly.

"Sorry? What for?"

"For putting you through all this again, but… oh, Carrie, maybe a boy this time?"

The blue line confirmed what my doctor had suspected – I really was pregnant!

properly and then leaned back in his chair. "Now then, Caroline, why don't you tell me what's really troubling you?"

"Oh, I'm fine. Missing Simon, of course. Tired and tearful, but I'm always a bit like this when he first goes away – I wondered if my thyroid was playing up."

"You read too many books!" He checked my blood pressure and then took some blood. "Let's just run a few tests anyway," he said as he slid the rubber-topped phials into an envelope. "What's your date of birth?"

I told him. He said "Hmmmn" in a very meaningful way and asked a few more rather personal questions.

"You think I'm menopausal? Or depressed? I'm – "

"Probably pregnant," he said with a smile, looking up at me from the form he was writing.

Even before the GP's tests came back, I'd nipped off to the chemist and got one of those test kits and the blue line confirmed what the doctor had guessed. Positive. Pregnant. Oh, my goodness, at forty-one!

Simon got a call through from the Middle East later in the week. I hadn't told Alison, because I wanted Simon to be the first to hear the news. He was

Alison was very quiet for a few minutes when I finally told her. I knew she was remembering the awful accusations she'd made.

She'd disposed of the roses from the study and I hadn't said a word. We both wanted to forget what she'd said.

At last she came over and hugged me. A real all-enveloping hug, which was very unusual these days, when she could be so wooden and moody.

"I'm not really so sure what to say, Mum," she mumbled. "But at least it's you and not me!"

We laughed at that, and the laughter

Would we be together as long?

helped a lot. Soon she relaxed and began talking about redecorating rooms and names and birth signs. The more we talked, the more enthusiastic she became and after about ten minutes I knew she was just itching to get onto Facebook and tell all her friends.

"Go on then, use Dad's computer," I said, but to my astonishment, she shook her head solemnly.

"If I hadn't sneaked into Dad's study that day, I wouldn't have seen those roses and that card and jumped to those awful conclusions. I don't want to use it, not when he's not here."

A couple of months passed. The Lamberts came home, and Cecily wasn't even on sticks after her lengthy protracted rehabilitation.

She and Bill came over to visit on the Sunday morning and she laughingly told me that breaking her leg was the best

of dark red, nearly black roses, papery and perfect, tied with one of her hair ribbons. "These are yours," she said, holding them out to Bill with a shy smile. "For Mrs Lambert."

"Mine?" Bill looked at her, puzzled. He reached out to take them and with one finger touched several of the beautiful petals. "Dried," he murmured. "Good Lord, they're perfect – only dried."

"My walk-in wardrobe backs on to the airing cupboard," Alison said. "We couldn't bear to throw them away, could we, Mum? I hung them upside down…" She looked at me and blushed again. I flashed her an understanding smile.

There were tears in Bill's eyes as he turned and presented the bouquet of roses to his wife. "Happy anniversary again, love," he said.

Cecily took the bouquet. She held it for

She looked at me and blushed again and I flashed her an understanding smile

answer to the hip op waiting list she'd ever come across. "And we're going on a cruise of the Norwegian Fjords for our golden anniversary treat – it's a bit delayed, but well worth the wait. We'll bring you back a troll, Alison!"

"Fiftieth anniversary," Alison repeated slowly. She looked at me and went red. And then she perked up. "I've got something for you both."

She was suddenly up and gone and running up the stairs. We heard her rummaging around in one of her cupboards and then she came thundering back. The smile on her face was truly beautiful. In her hands she held a bunch

a moment, then carefully undid the ribbon and removed half a dozen of the beautiful red-black blooms. She handed them back to Alison. "For your mum," she said. "Until your dad gets back to give her red roses of her own."

A WORD FROM THE AUTHOR

"Before they were over, I hung my bunch of red roses upside down in the airing cupboard. Weeks later I had another perfect bouquet – dried – which lasted for many months more."

Two Teatime

Blueberry Blondies

MAKES CHUNKY PIECES

VANILLA & FRUIT

Ingredients
- 300g (10oz) white chocolate chips
- 100g (3 ½oz) butter
- 175g (6oz) self raising flour
- 175g (6oz) ground almonds
- 175g (6oz) caster sugar
- 4 medium eggs, beaten
- 1tsp vanilla extract
- 150g (5oz) fresh blueberries

Preparation time: 20mins plus cooling
Cooking time: 40mins
Makes 12

● Preheat the oven to 180°C, Fan Oven 160°C, Gas Mark 4. Grease and line an 18 x 28cm (7 x 11inch) rectangular cake tin. Put 125g (4oz) **chocolate chips** in a heatproof bowl and add the **butter**. Place the bowl over a saucepan of gently simmering water to melt the contents. Remove from the heat and cool for 10mins.

● Sift the **flour** into another bowl and stir in the **almonds**, **sugar** and remaining chocolate chips. Make a well in the centre and gradually mix in the **eggs**, **vanilla** and melted chocolate mixture to form a thick batter. Carefully fold in the fresh **blueberries**.

● Spoon into the prepared tin and smooth over the top. Bake in the oven for about 40mins until risen, just firm, and lightly golden. Allow to cool in the tin before cutting into 12 pieces. Carefully remove from the tin and store in an airtight container for up to 5 days.

WORDS AND FOOD STYLING: KATHRYN HAWKINS PHOTOGRAPHY: LIGHTHOUSE PHOTOGRAPHY

Treats For You!

Macaroons

Ingredients

- 3 large egg whites
- 75g (3oz) caster sugar
- 300g (10oz) icing sugar
- 125g (4oz) ground almonds
- A few drops of your favourite food colourings
- 75g (3oz) unsalted butter, softened

Preparation time:
30mins plus cooling
Cooking time:
50mins
Makes 16

IMPRESS YOUR GUESTS

ADD FUN COLOURS

- Preheat the oven to 150°C, Fan Oven 130°C, Gas Mark 2. Line 4 large baking sheets with baking parchment. In a clean, grease-free bowl, whisk the **egg whites** until very stiff, then whisk in the **caster sugar** to make a thick, glossy meringue.

- Sieve over 175g (6oz) **icing sugar**, and then sift the **ground almonds** on top to remove any lumps. Gently fold into the meringue mix. Divide the mixture between different bowls, and add your chosen **food colouring**.

- Spoon the mixture into individual piping bags fitted with 1cm (½inch) plain nozzles. Pipe rounds spaced apart, on to the baking sheets – you should be able to make 32 rounds. Bake two trays at a time on the low and middle shelves for about 25mins, swapping the trays round half-way through until crisp and only lightly coloured. Cool on the baking sheets before peeling away from the baking parchment.

- Put the **butter** in a bowl and add in remaining icing sugar, to make icing. Add a few drops of food colouring and sandwich the macaroons together.

More Fish In The Sea

The herring trade was tough – until a disaster turned those silver darlings into a gold mine for Minna and her family…

By Mary Kettlewell

Us Girvans have been a herring family through and through for generations. A hard life it is, too, and every penny earned means a back-breaking twelve-hour day. My story begins in 1843 in a ramshackle cottage in the village of North Scar that's home to me and my grandparents.

"Where's Granfer?"

"Been gone since four, Minna," said Gran, stirring her stew. "A man of his years shouldn't be braving that east wind so early. But he's worried where the next

strong bond, but hardship puts a strain on things." The sadness in her voice tore at my heart. Mother and Father had caught the smallpox when I was a bairn and my grandparents had brought me up.

"I'll be away now, Gran. The boats will be coming in on the high tide."

How the east wind bit into us herring lassies that day! Bonnie waved her hands in the air. "That's me done. Me hands are frozen solid!" she said before scuttling off. I was about to follow when steps rang out on the cobbles. A tall, muscular skipper was staggering up the

I could see him looking at me beneath my bonnet and felt myself flushing

penny'll come from – and hoping for an early buyer on his herring stall. "

"I can do more hours at the herring gutting if it'll help, Gran."

She shook her head. "There's limits to what even a young body like yours can stand. Don't fret, his curtness isn't for you, child. He loves you with all his heart."

"And does he love you, Gran? For he's always finding fault."

"Forty years of married life makes for a

slope under the weight of a boxful of wriggling silver darlings.

"Lazy devils, that crew o' mine. Left these in the hold. Would you do me a kindness and gut them, lassie? Double pay." He chinked the coins in his purse.

My heart sank – but I knew I couldn't turn down good money.

"You've cut your poor hands to bits, lass." His voice was filled with concern.

"Ay, sir. It's the numbing cold makes

Herring lassies worked on, even in the bitter cold

the knife slip." I picked up the first herring. Slash, and out tumbled the guts into the barrel. Two… three… a dozen…

"Maybe you can help me, lassie. I'm looking for a place to rent in the village, where I can store the catch overnight."

"My granfer has two sheds. Full of old fish boxes and the like. It's the first cottage up the alley and past the jetty. Girvan's the name. Jeremiah Girvan."

"And yours, lassie?" I could see him looking at me beneath my bonnet and I felt myself flushing.

"Minna, they call me," I muttered.

"Well, now, Minna, you tell your grandfather that Logan McFadden, skipper of the Farne Maiden, will be up to see him first thing the morn." He put his hand into his pocket and pressed three silver sixpences into my frozen hand.

"Granfer, there's a skipper McFadden **Continued overleaf…**

of the Farne Maiden wants to rent your sheds. New to the fishing here, he is. He's calling at first light if that's all right."

Granfer looked up from his pipe and scowled. "And what am I supposed to do with all the old nets and boxes, girl?"

Gran threw thyme into the stewpot. "Go on with you, Jeremiah. I've long told you those sheds want a clearout."

"Always fretting, you are," he muttered, sending a cloud of smoke from his pipe.

Granfer eyed him beneath his bushy brows. "I'd find no fault with that."

Logan nodded. "And what would you be asking for the rent, sir?"

"Nothing for now, Mr McFadden, but how does a shilling the week sound once I've cleared out all the junk?"

I took one look at his tired eyes and his frail body with its bowed shoulders.

"I'll see to it, Granfer," I offered.

Logan broke in firmly with, "Not on

I have to admit my heart skipped a beat when I learned that he was unmarried

"We can't afford to turn down good money, Jeremiah, and well you know it."

I feared harsh words and shouting, so I stepped forward quickly. "There's this to help with the food and rent, Gran." I held out the three shiny sixpences in my palm.

Her eyes widened in astonishment. "It's not reckoning day yet. How did you come by them, Minna?"

"Skipper McFadden found a box of fish his crew had missed. He offered me double pay to gut them and asked if I knew where he could store his fish."

Gran looked at me in that way she has, head on one side, eyes thoughtful.

I flushed under her gaze but was saved from questioning by Granfer pulling me over to his chair. "You're a fine girl, Minna. What would we do without you?"

I felt a tear in the corner of my eye as his words went right to my heart.

I'll rent the two sheds, Jeremiah Girvan. They're just the job for my silver darlings. But there's another request. I've a load of old oak spars off wrecked ships. What say you if I stack them on your land? They'd make a tidy third shed."

your own, lass. I'll give you a hand."

Granfer started to protest, but Gran's voice was soft and insistent. "Leave them be, Jeremiah." Then she turned back to her stewpot, but not before I caught the soft smile that touched her lips.

Soon we were rolling up lengths of ancient netting, heaving out broken boxes and chattering away as if we'd known each other from childhood.

"What's it like, the fishing, Logan?"

"Hard work, rough seas and the Northumberland sandbanks to keep a sharp weather eye on."

"And the storms?"

"You've no time to feel fear, lass. Not when there's gigantic waves crashing over the boat's bows."

"It must be a worry for your wife and bairns. You out in all weathers."

He laughed gently. "I haven't got a wife. It wouldn't be right to put a woman and bairns to such worries."

I have to admit that my heart skipped a beat when I learned that he was free.

"I'll knit you a fisherman's gansey to keep out the cold," I said shyly, running my eye over his patched reefer jacket.

A hard life on the seas

bag, Granfer looked across, his eyes crinkling with humour.

"What's that you're knitting, Minna?"

"A gansey, Granfer."

"For me, lass, eh?"

I gave no answer, for he knew full well who the gansey was for.

Then just when it seemed the sun had come out from a dark cloud for our family, disaster struck.

It was barely four and the sun not yet up when I smelled burning. I threw back the shutters and peered out. The sheds were full of Logan's herrings, laid neatly in boxes or flat trays waiting for the morning market. Smoke was eddying in a dense cloud from the nearest shed.

I ran barefoot across the dew-damp grass and stared in horror. Those boxes of herrings laid close to the fire were sizzling and spitting where sparks had alighted. They were now smoke-blackened and all utterly ruined.

Then I became aware that my grandparents were standing behind me in their nightwear. Granfer's face was grey as ash, while Gran dabbed at her eyes with a kerchief – and I knew it was not the smoke that was causing the tears.

"That's a kindly offer, Minna. One that no woman's ever made me before. I'll pay for the wool, mind. And what about you – have you a young man?"

I took a rag and wiped the window, trying to hide my blushes from him. "Oh, I've been friendly with one or two lads in the past…" I said, overcome with shyness.

"And now?" He looked keenly at me.

"I'll knit you a fisherman's gansey to keep out the cold," I offered shyly

"No one," I whispered, though I knew from the way he picked up a joist of timber and hurled it out of the door that my words pleased him.

The offer of a steady rent lifted a huge burden from my grandparents' shoulders. When I took out the balls of thick dark blue wool from my knitting

"We'll have to pay him for the fish," he said and his voice was flat, empty.

"It'll take the last of our savings, Jeremiah. God be praised I've yet two sovereigns stashed away in the kitchen."

"He'll be storming with anger and he won't rent any more for sure." Granfer rubbed a hand over his bristly chin.

Continued overleaf…

"I'll go down to the harbour and meet him when the Farne Maiden comes in." I could barely hold back the tears.

An hour, maybe more, I waited in the damp cold of the morning.

As he jumped ashore and tied the boat to a bollard he said, "Why, Minna, what's up, lassie? You're white as a sheet."

"It's bad news, Logan…" I began

"Let's get this mess cleared." He hunched his powerful shoulders and made to lift the nearest tray of burnt herrings. Then he started sniffing.

"Well, I'll be darned!" he exclaimed. "That's a tasty smell if ever there was one." He held up a herring by its tail.

Granfer took a long, deep sniff. "Ay, Logan, you're right, it's a fine smell."

My heart beat furiously as I waited for the flurry of angry words from him

breathlessly "… a pile of oak spars and some chippings caught fire in the night. The smoke has ruined your herring catch." I went on, blurting out the words. "Granfer'll pay you the full cost."

My heart was beating furiously as I stood there waiting for the flurry of angry words. Instead he stepped forward and put his arm round my shoulders.

"Minna, my dear girl, had it been you or your grandparents that were damaged in the fire, my heart would have been heavy indeed. But herrings? There's plenty more o' those in God's oceans."

I wanted to press my cheek against Logan's rough, stubbly chin.

"You're not angry?" I whispered.

"Angry? I'm just relieved that you're all safe and sound."

Granfer was standing by the shed with Gran. They were both upset. "Your catch is ruined, Mr McFadden, but we'll repay every penny, never fear."

Logan threw back his head and laughed. "You'll do no such thing, Jeremiah Girvan. And no more of that 'Mr McFadden' – it's plain Logan."

Gran was holding out her money box, two sovereigns glinting in her hand but he brushed it away with a smile.

Gran came next, her nose wrinkling. "Fancy that. A burnt fish that's sweet and smokey like a smouldering pine log."

Logan pulled a piece of flesh from the herring and gingerly put it into his mouth. His face broke into the broadest of grins. "It tastes even better than it smells! Here, have a taste yourself, Minna, lass."

Fish turned to gold

Hesitanty, I took a piece of the charred herring. And I wouldn't have believed it, so tangy and delicious was its flavour.

Logan was stomping around fit to bust. "What say we throw some oak shavings on to the fire and hang a row of herrings on the smoke-ward side overnight? I'll take them down to the fishermen at the harbour to try. They'll never have sailed before with such a tasty breakfast in their bellies, I'll warrant."

"And what think you to call them, Logan?" Granfer asked. "Black darlings?"

Gran shook her head. "Nae, Jeremiah. Something to call folks' attention to that rich, deep brown colour they've taken on."

"Kippers," I said shyly. "Like coppers, only a bit different."

Logan slapped his thigh. "That's it, lass. Short, sharp with all the salt, smoke and flavour in the word. Kippers it is!"

And there in the sight of Gran and Granfer, he put his arms round me, the

with a handful of herbs thrown in. There's meat aplenty now and, of course, kippers and silver darlings to ring the changes.

And me? Already the cuts and scars on my hands have all but disappeared and herring gutting is a thing of the past.

I'm in the kipper business now, too, and I take a pride in hanging them row by row in our new smoke houses. Sixteen hours' smoking does them to a turn.

Logan has sold the Farne Maiden. Every day he auctions the kippers and now that the gentry have taken a fancy to them, the price goes up and up.

Handsome in his new blue gansey, he's banging and hammering away at a wooden house set on the leeward side of the sheds well away from the smoke. For, as he says, I won't want to live my married life in a kipper house! Brides-to-be should smell of honeysuckle and roses, not oak smoke and ashes.

As for the wedding breakfast, Granfer

And there in sight of Gran and Granfer he put his arms around me and kissed me!

kipper still dangling from his fingers and crushed my lips to his! But I needn't have worried, for when we finally finished our kiss, there were Gran and Granfer holding hands and pecking each other's cheeks.

A year's gone by and there are four sheds in the garden now, with a big board at the front written in red letters. GIRVAN AND MCFADDEN – KIPPER WHOLESALERS.

Granfer's sold his fish stall and bought himself a whole new rack of pipes and a rocking chair to sit by the fire. Gran delights in spending her time cooking for her new family. Not just vegetable stews

says we must have kippers, but I can tell Gran's not so sure. "Go on with you, Jeremiah. Such foolish talk. Whoever heard of kippers at a wedding feast?"

Logan and I have decided to let them sort it out for themselves, for we're just as happy either way!

ILLUSTRATIONS: JAMES DEWAR, DAVID MATYSIAK

A Few Precious Words

Life is so intense when we're teenagers, but some special friendships we never outgrow

By Elizabeth McKay

The doorbell rang just as Julie was loading the dishwasher.

"Put the kettle on, Sis," said Tessa, breezing through the hallway into the kitchen. "I've brought the éclairs. It's ages since we've had a proper gossip."

They sat at the kitchen table, swapping moans, starting with errant husbands before moving on to other subjects, like kids, clothes, money – or rather, the lack of it – and what their mutual friends were getting up to these days.

"I nearly forgot," Tessa said before she left. "Did you read the death notices in the local paper yesterday?"

you and I weren't listening to records in Rosemary's room then we were experimenting with make-up in ours."

"Do you think Rosemary will come home for the funeral?" Julie asked.

"I'm sure she will. She was very close to her mother, even after she moved to live in Canada."

"It would be good to see her again," said Julie thoughtfully.

"And of course Patrick will be there," added Tessa.

"Patrick! Do you think he'll take the service himself?"

Tessa shook her head seriously. "I shouldn't think so. After all it would be too much of an ordeal, don't you think? Taking your own mother's funeral."

"You're not still pining after the lovely Patrick, are you?" Julie's sister teased

Julie shook her head sadly. "I never read them. Not since Mum…"

Tessa nodded. "Then you won't know that Mrs O'Connell died last week. The funeral's this Tuesday, at St Stephen's. I think we should go."

"But we haven't seen her for years."

"I know. But I think Mum would want us to go. They were neighbours for a long time and they still kept in touch after the O'Connells moved away. And there was a time when we were growing up that we practically lived in each other's houses. If

"Do you really think we should go?" Julie asked. "Perhaps they just want family and close friends."

"The notice said everyone was welcome," replied Tessa. "Like I said, I think Mum would want us to."

Julie sighed and said nothing.

"What's up, Sis?" Tessa laughed. "You're not still pining after the lovely Patrick, are you?"

"Of course not," Julie snapped. "We were just kids back then."

"That's settled then," said Tessa. "I'll

Julie had to tell Patrick that she loved him

pick you up on Tuesday at ten, sharp."

Tessa and Rosemary were having another argument. This time it was about who was better looking – Donny Osmond or David Cassidy.

Julie sat on the edge of Rosemary's bed and flicked absentmindedly through the latest copy of Jackie magazine. She **Continued overleaf…**

couldn't see the attraction herself.

There was a loud rap on the door and Patrick stuck his head round and yelled, "How am I supposed to study for my exams with you lot shrieking like an entire tribe of banshees?"

"I'm telling Mum you yelled at us," said Rosemary, flicking her auburn curls.

"You can tell Mum whatever you like," replied her brother. "She'll say the same as me. If you really can't keep quiet then

Rosemary treats him. He's just trying to do well in his exams, that's all."

"And then you know what'll happen, don't you?" Tessa didn't wait for an answer. "If he passes, he'll go to university and meet lots of girls and marry one and he'll forget all about dear little Julie from next door."

"I said shut up," Julie yelled again, this time adding weight to her argument by throwing a stuffed panda at her sister.

He'll go to university, meet lots of girls and forget about little Julie next door

you'll all have to go somewhere else."

"Sorry, Patrick," said Julie in a small and shy voice. "We'll be quiet from now on, I promise."

Patrick smiled at her before disappearing back to his own room.

"Don't you think he's absolutely gorgeous, Julie?" asked Rosemary.

"Yes, he is," Julie replied, not realising her friend was referring to the David Cassidy poster in her hand.

Later that night when Julie and Tessa were getting ready for bed in the room they shared, Tessa turned away from the mirror and faced Julie.

"You fancy Patrick O'Connell," she chanted accusingly.

"I do not," Julie stuttered, but she could feel her face burning.

"Yes, you do. I saw the way you looked at him today." Tessa dropped her head to the side and adopted a simpering voice. "I'm so sorry Patrick, darling. I promise we'll be quiet from now on, darling, darling Patrick."

"Shut up," Julie yelled, almost crying with humiliation. "Patrick's nice, that's all. I just think it's a shame the way

The next time she saw Patrick she was on her own. Tessa and Rosemary were at a school disco. Julie, being a year younger, wasn't eligible to go.

She was coming back from visiting her gran when Patrick came out of the corner shop carrying a folded newspaper.

Julie's heart began doing funny fluttering things. At first she prayed Patrick wouldn't walk with her and then she prayed he would.

"Hi Julie." He smiled and fell into step with her. "How come you're not at the disco with our sisters?"

"You've got to be fifteen to be allowed in," she muttered shyly.

"Right," he said, nodding in agreement. "I keep forgetting you're younger than the other two. You always seem to be so much more sensible than the pair of them put together."

Julie dipped her head and studied her shoes so that her hair made a curtain to hide her face. Her heart was beating so hard now, it almost hurt. *Was it possible to have a heart attack at fourteen*, she thought silently?

"Here," suddenly Patrick's hand was in

She sealed it with a kiss

Patrick ✗

"That's okay." He smiled. "I can see you're disappointed at not getting to the disco with the others."

Patrick got a job working at a holiday camp on the south coast. Rosemary updated her friends whenever he sent a postcard home.

"What about a girlfriend?" Tessa asked, glancing at Julie out of the corner of her eye. "Does he say anything about having a girlfriend?"

Rosemary made a face.

"What girl in her right mind would go out with my brother?"

"What do you think, Julie?" asked Tessa, now openly teasing her younger sister. "Do you think Patrick's good looking? Would you go out with him?"

"Don't be daft, Tess," giggled Rosemary, linking her friend's arm. "Patrick's nearly eighteen. He's not going to go out with a little kid, is he?"

Julie said nothing and prayed her blush hadn't given her away before she hid behind her long fringe.

It was a long, hot summer that year. The girls were sunbathing in the park,

front of her face, "have some chocolate. I'm celebrating the end of my exams."

"Did you do okay?" she asked timidly.

He shrugged. "Won't know for a few weeks yet. In the meantime I've got to find myself a summer job." He waved the newspaper. "I can't see there being much on offer around here though. I'll probably have to move away."

"Move away?" she jerked her head up and stared at him, almost panic-striken.

"Bye then, Julie," Patrick said, pushing another chocolate bar into her hand

"I might not have much choice," he replied. "I've got to earn at least some cash before I start college."

They walked the rest of the way in awkward silence before they eventually arrived at Julie's gate.

"Bye then, Julie," Patrick said, pushing another chocolate bar into her hand.

"Thanks Patrick," she beamed at him.

listening to Radio One on Rosemary's transistor, when she suddenly sat up.

"I nearly forgot to tell you," she said, "Patrick got his exam results yesterday. He did really well and he's starting college after the holidays."

"Lucky Patrick," said Tessa lazily, lying on her front, soaking up the rays. "Just **Continued overleaf…**

Continued from previous page

imagine not having parents telling you what to do all the time. I expect he'll meet lots of girls, fall in love with one of them and get married."

"That's the other thing I was going to tell you," said Rosemary, "it's not an ordinary college. It's a seminary. Patrick's going to be a priest."

Tessa sat up straight and stared first at Rosemary and then at Julie. "A priest? You mean he'll never be able to get

She'd probably never see him.

So she wrote him a letter. She poured out everything that was on her heart. Sealed it with a kiss, and carefully wrote Patrick on the front of the envelope, then pushed it through the letterbox one night when she was supposed to be in bed.

She waited for him to call on her the next day, and the next. At the end of the week Rosemary announced Patrick had left on the overnight sleeper and her

Julie had waited for Patrick to call on her but she'd probably never see him again

married – not even if he falls in love?"

"Priests don't fall in love," replied Rosemary matter-of-factly.

Julie said nothing at all. But she thought about it for days. She'd read in books that sometimes women entered convents to recover from broken hearts – could it be the same for priests?

If only she'd been more encouraging that day when he'd walked her home from the shop. If only she'd been more enthusiastic about the chocolate, saying it was her favourite kind, even though it was plain and she preferred milk. If only she'd been able to think of something witty to say when he'd commented about how immature Tessa and Rosemary were.

She had to let him know that it wasn't too late. That he didn't have to waste his life in a seminary. That she loved him.

She knew he was coming home for a week before he went to the seminary. Rosemary had said her mother was planning all sorts of family parties before he left.

parents had applied to the council for a smaller house as they didn't need an extra bedroom any more.

Mrs O'Connell's funeral was three days ago. Rosemary had invited Julie and Tessa back to the house. It was good seeing her again. Patrick was there too. He'd shaken hands warmly with both

Patrick had left to become a priest

of them, thanked them for coming and apologised for not being able to spend much time with them as he had to mingle with the other mourners.

The next day, Julie was emptying the dishwasher when the doorbell rang.

"I hope this isn't a bad time," Patrick said, standing on the doorstep.

"I wanted to thank you for coming to the funeral," he said, sitting at the kitchen table while Julie fidgeted with coffee mugs and cakes. "I'm sorry I didn't hear about your own mother's death until Rosemary told me last night."

"When does Rosemary go back to Canada?" Julie asked, finally running out of excuses not to sit down opposite him.

"She's on her way now," he said, "I've just taken her to the airport. There was no point in staying on after we'd sorted out Mum's things."

"It's not an easy job," Julie sighed.

"I found this," Patrick said, taking a

He laughed softly. "Then she ought to have known better. She knew how much I dreamed of entering the priesthood. It was all I ever wanted since I was a boy."

"Then I understand why she did what she did." Julie smiled at him.

She wasn't fourteen any more. She was a grown woman with a family of her own. "If I was in her position I'd do the same."

Suddenly the atmosphere became more relaxed and they were talking like the old friends they were.

"What about this?" Patrick said, nodding to the letter as he rose to leave.

Julie smiled. "You decide."

Patrick crushed the letter in his fist and dropped it in Julie's recycling box behind the kitchen door.

Julie waved him off then returned to the kitchen and retrieved the ball of paper from the box. She placed it on the table and gently smoothed it with her flat hand before taking it upstairs and placing it carefully inside the toffee tin where she

The atmosphere relaxed and they talked like the old friends that they were

crumpled envelope from his pocket and placing it on the table.

Julie's heart lurched.

"I didn't know," he said quietly. "I only read it for the first time yesterday. I had no idea you felt the way you did."

"It was just a silly schoolgirl crush." Julie's voice quivered.

"All the same," he replied. "The least you deserved was a reply. Mum was wrong to keep it from me."

"I suppose that's why she was so keen to move house after you left," Julie said. "So there wouldn't be any temptations when you came home on holiday."

kept her most precious things. Things like locks of the children's hair and drawings they'd done at school.

And the crumpled wrapper of a chocolate bar given to her when she was just fourteen years old.

A WORD FROM THE AUTHOR

"A friend gave me this idea when she told me about a childhood crush she had on her friend's brother who broke her heart when he left to be a priest."

Bee Mine

Organised, cool and unflappable, Kirstie was determined her brother's grand wedding would go without a hitch…

By Joanna Barnden

Bees!" Kirstie's brother screamed down the phone. "We've got bees!"

"Bees?" Kirstie asked calmly, excusing herself from the board meeting with a discreet wave of her hand. "Is that a problem?"

Half the directors must have heard her brother's incredulous gasp through the telephone receiver.

"Is it a problem, Kirstie? It's a nightmare! The men can't put the marquee up because they keep getting stung. Apparently there's a nest under your eaves."

James sounded rather accusatory but then, Kirstie reminded herself charitably, he was under a lot of pressure. He was getting married in two days and had the perfect wedding planned for his bride – and now he had bees. Or, rather, she did. Rueing the day she'd ever agreed to let them use her lawn for this grand event, Kirstie took a few yogic breaths and addressed her panicking brother.

"Keep calm, James. Just ring the council. They'll put you in touch with a pest-controller and he'll get rid of them in no time, I'm sure."

"But Kirstie, what about the marquee?"

Kirstie tutted.

"Tell them to put long sleeves on and get on with it."

"But it's thirty degrees out here."

Kirstie cast an eye towards the big windows of her beautiful boardroom and saw that somewhere beyond the air-con and the tinted glass, the sun was indeed belting down.

"It'll be lovely for the wedding," she said blithely.

"Kirstie, I need help!"

"Okay, okay." She glanced at her watch. "I'll be there in an hour."

"An hour?"

"Just get the man in, James, okay?"

"Okay, sis," James said nervously.

Kirstie was rueing the day she'd agreed to let them use her lawn for this event

Kirstie clicked off her phone and turned back to the meeting with an apologetic smile.

"Marquee crisis," she explained.

There were knowing nods around the table. Despite the size of Kirstie's company she'd always sought to keep the personal touch and her five directors were as much friends as colleagues. They were all coming to the wedding – a condition of using her lawn – and had been involved in much of the build-up. James's **Continued overleaf…**

high expectations, muddled approach and tendency to panic easily had been the subject of much amusement for their calm business heads over the last months.

Kirstie had set up her childcare agency five years ago when her older sister, Maggie, had been tearing her hair out trying to find a nursery for her new baby. It had found a market straight away and under Kirstie's expert and ruthless guidance, it had gone from strength to strength. Now it was a national network and Kirstie employed over 100 people directly and acted as agent for some 1500 more. She loved her job above all else in her life, but her little brother came a very close second.

"I'm going to have to go and bail him out," Kirstie said now, "so let's try and

Even the bees couldn't resist her beautiful home

Continued overleaf…

wrap this meeting up pronto," she added.

The board put their heads down and swiftly and efficiently despatched the remaining items on the agenda.

As she concluded the meeting, Kirstie smiled with satisfaction. Her family all thought she was strange, a bit cold even, to be so devoted to her career, but she truly loved it.

And so what if talk inevitably turned to the irritating "and who'll be next then?"

bees. At the other end of the garden five burly blokes stood watching from behind a pile of marquee supports. Somewhere in the middle, looking anxious, was James.

Ignoring her brother, she strode over to the men. She saw them clock her arrival and was glad she was in her smartest – and shortest – Nicole Fahri suit.

"You're the men erecting this marquee, are you?" she demanded as they all rather hastily stubbed out cigarettes.

Her family all thought she was strange, cold even, but she loved her career

whenever James's wedding came up? Look at him in a state now because his Emily would panic if the marquee wasn't up when she got back from the hairdressers. And look at Maggie, two kids around her feet and so heavily pregnant again that she'd suggested hiring a second marquee for her to wear on the big day!

Why would Kirstie want all the muddle and mess of falling in love when, instead, she could have a profitable business, a fast car and a house so beautiful James had literally begged her to use it? A house so beautiful, it seemed, that even bees couldn't resist it.

Kirstie screeched into her driveway and pulled up beside a neat white van with "Bug-busters" written across the side in stripy script. James had managed to do something himself then!

She strode around the side of her lovely old Georgian house and surveyed the scene. Above her, on the little balcony she'd had built onto her study, a man wearing what looked like a space suit was doing battle with an angry swarm of

"That's right, Miss," two said in unison.

"Or, in fact, the men not erecting this marquee, correct?"

The foreman shifted awkwardly.

"Er, no. There's bees, see…"

"Bees?"

Kirstie allowed a small raise of her perfectly sugared eyebrow to convey her disdain of such tiny insects.

"They sting!" he protested.

"So do I," Kirstie said in a low voice, "so I suggest you get on with your job. If you need extra clothing I'm sure I can provide it."

A sudden image of these beer-bellied men in her silky tops and cashmere cardigans made Kirstie want to laugh out loud, but she bit it back behind her best boss's stare. They crumpled.

"We'll be fine, Miss. That bloke's about got them now anyway."

"Good. I'll be back soon to check on your progress."

She moved back towards the house, hearing the pleasing clink of poles behind her as she went. James ran up and grabbed her hands.

"Thanks Kirstie, you're a life-saver!

He was not what she was expecting at all

veil of dark mesh and nodded.

"Great," he said, his low voice strangely amplified by his headgear. "I've got the Queen so the rest should follow naturally."

"Cup of tea?" Kirstie suggested.

"Please. Thirsty work this. I'll be down in five."

Kirstie went into her elegant shaker kitchen and put the kettle on. She glanced at her watch. A quick drink with this old bug-buster to make sure all was well and then she'd get going. She had a lot of work to get through this afternoon.

She reached for the tea bags, rejecting her usual Earl Grey, then found the sugar bowl – tradesmen always wanted sugar – and poured out two cups.

Emily will be ever so grateful to you."

Kirstie smiled. She liked her brother's wife-to-be. Emily was small and lively and had a sense of humour as wicked as Kirstie's. She was also, sadly, as scatty as James and it would be a miracle if their wedding went off smoothly – her miracle.

"I'll just check on the bee-man then," she said, "and then get back to work for an hour or two."

James nodded.

"Great. I've got to get to the printers. Slight glitch with the orders of service."

Kirstie felt her eyebrows raise again as

He came past the window just as she was setting the pot down. She moved to open the French doors but he had his back to her and was peeling off his protective gear. Kirstie blinked. As the big boiler suit fell to the floor a young, toned body in neat shorts and a startlingly white T-shirt emerged. She held her breath as muscled arms reached up to lift off the helmet and was rewarded by a shock of sandy hair and, as the bug-man turned, a pair of indecently blue eyes and a wide, throat-

As the big boiler suit fell to the floor a young, toned body emerged from it

James thankfully escaped. She looked up at her study. The bee-man had a large box which he'd set up on her balcony and into which he was trying, with some success it seemed, to coax the insects.

"Everything okay up there?" she called.

He looked down at her through a large

catching smile. Kirstie gulped as he stepped through the doors and reached gratefully for the mug she was holding out.

"Sugar?" she managed.

"No thanks, evil stuff." He took a big glug. "Lovely – cheers! I'm Nick by the way."

Continued overleaf…

Continued from previous page

frown, "they'll be gone by tomorrow. It'll be fine for your wedding."

"Oh, it's not my wedding," she said, a little too quickly.

"No?" he said with a wry smile.

"No, it's my brother's."

"Oh. So why are you here then?"

She drew herself up a little.

"It's my house," she replied.

"Yours?" Nick's eyebrows shot up and he glanced around, no doubt looking for the big-earning husband.

Kirstie bristled. "All mine," she said, rather smugly.

He gave a low whistle.

"You must be a very successful woman, Kirstie. Ruthless too, no doubt?"

Was he teasing her? She wasn't sure.

"This isn't Dallas you know," she retorted. "I can get a job done, yes, but I'm not some calculating, obsessive, man-hating harridan."

She kicked herself. Why had she said that? Nick, however, just grinned.

"Glad to hear it. You off back to work now you've sorted us all out then?"

Kirstie shifted.

"I thought I might work from home actually. That's the beauty of running your own business – you can be so flexible."

"You can," he agreed easily. "When I first started out I was working for the council and had to do exactly what I was

"Em… Kirstie," she managed as Nick casually leant back against her antique pine table, seemingly completely immersed in his drink.

She felt herself beginning to melt and had to glance down at her suit to remind herself that she was a top business-woman and not a star-struck girl.

"All sorted then?" she asked crisply.

She glanced at her suit to remind herself that she was not a star-struck girl

"We're getting there. It's all about psychology with bees."

Nick smiled again and Kirstie's stomach did silly loops. *Top businesswoman* she told it sternly. It ignored her.

"Don't worry," he said, seeing her

told. These days I'm freer. There's a lot more admin, mind you."

"There is?" She raised one eyebrow.

"Oh yes. It's a nightmare – 23 bug-busters don't just organise themselves you know!"

He grinned at her then, with a wink, he

was gone, leaving Kirstie with her mouth hanging open. Horrified at herself she snapped it shut and headed for her desk.

Kirstie got little work done that afternoon. It was hard concentrating with the bangs and chinks of the rapidly emerging marquee below her and the soft drone of confused bees, not to mention the thud of her own heart every time she saw Nick the bee-man outside her windows.

Eventually he tapped on the balcony door. She let him in as he shed his outer gear again. He looked hot but triumphant.

"Got them," he told her. "There's a few still buzzing about but they'll soon go without the Queen."

"Thank you so much," Kirstie said. "It would have been awful if they'd come out on the big day."

"No worries there now. Enjoy it."

She felt sudden panic as he moved to assemble his gear and leave.

"Exactly – that's what makes it fun!"

She looked at Nick. He was laughing but not at her, and his eyes were soft. Below she heard a squeal of delight as Emily arrived and saw her marquee.

"Maybe fun," she agreed slowly.

"Is that a yes, then?"

But Kirstie wasn't so easily won.

"They'll pester you," she warned. "My family will all want to know who you are, what you do, and if you'll be walking me up the aisle soon."

He chuckled.

"I'll tell them: I'm Nick, I run a public service company, and maybe I will."

She stared at him.

"There's only one way to find out, isn't there?" he added with a wink.

Below them Kirstie saw her brother come up gently behind his bride, hugging her in close against him and smiling as their dream took shape before them. Complicated, messy, out of control…?

"They'll pester you. My family will all want to know who you are, what you do"

"You must come," she blurted out.

He turned and looked straight at her.

"As a date?" he asked, grinning.

"As a thank you."

"I think I'd prefer it as a date."

Kirstie tried to keep her smile buried, but it defied her usually expert control and broke out anyway.

"I don't usually do dating," she said uncharacteristically self-conscious.

"Why not?" he asked plainly.

"It can get so complicated."

"Fun though."

"And messy."

"But fun, hey?" He grinned again.

"And… and out of control."

"There's only one way to find out," Kirstie agreed.

After all, isn't that what she was always telling the board – there comes a time when you have to take a calculated risk. And Nick was one risk Kirstie calculated might just make her very happy.

A WORD FROM THE AUTHOR

"My brother's wedding was nearly held up by a bee's nest and I loved the image of muscled men cowering before tiny insects. The rest grew from there."

Pillow Talk

Sometimes the things that aren't said about a situation speak volumes, especially when it comes to family problems

By Sue Houghton

Pete seems to be in a good mood. It's Sunday morning and as usual, he's brought the newspapers up to bed. I'm thinking now would be a good time to speak to him about our daughter, Abby.

Pete's whistling comes to an abrupt halt as he stubs his toe on the pile of books that's being used to prop up the foot of the bed ever since the leg fell off.

I've been nagging him for ages about buying a new one and although the bed is less important than my news about our daughter, on balance, I think steering Pete and his wallet to the shops is going to be a lot easier than getting him to talk about Abby.

"I know that look, Mo," Pete says, climbing in beside me and nursing his sore toe. "You've got something playing on your mind."

I decided that maybe it'd be wise to considering a bedroom makeover…"

He grins at me. "I wasn't aware we were, Mo."

"Well, we are now. I'm not suggesting anything major. How about we give the woodwork a lick of paint? Strip the wallpaper. It's looking so dated. We haven't decorated this room since…"

"Since Abby left home."

I really hadn't been expecting that! "Gosh, yes," I say, pretending I hadn't realised. "Let's see. How long is it? Must be all of…"

He comes straight back with, "Three years, six months and one week."

I shouldn't really be surprised he knows the exact date she left home. Pete keeps a diary and I've seen him circle the anniversary each year.

"So, talking of Abby," I say, trying to make light of it.

"Like the makeover, I wasn't aware we were," he says, opening his newspaper. "Can we change the subject? You know

Yes, I do know how he feels – raising Abby had never been an easy job

start with the smaller issues first.

"Remember we talked about buying a new bed?" I say. "I thought we might finally get around to it this weekend. There's a sale on in town, so we might spot a bargain. And while we're

how I feel." And he turns his attention to the cryptic crossword.

Yes, I do know how he feels. Raising Abby had never been easy. Like most parents we went through the Terrible Twos, the Troublesome Threes, the

Frantic Fours… but it didn't stop there. On and on it went.

The teenage years were the worst but throughout it all we loved her dearly, hoping things would improve.

As she blossomed into a beautiful young woman, the rows between her and Pete especially grew worse. In particular about a young biker called Bad Hawk who she claimed she loved.

Maybe we didn't try hard enough to understand her.

On the morning of her seventeenth birthday, we found her bed hadn't been slept in. A brief note pinned to her favourite teddy informed us she'd gone to

"I know that look, Mo," Pete says

Continued overleaf…

"get herself a life" with Bad Hawk.

We rang, we wrote, desperate to keep the lines of communication open. Then silence. For over three years we didn't hear a thing.

Pete copes by refusing to speak of her, though I know he thinks about her every day. So do I.

Many a time I've spotted a young woman across a busy street and been the worst. And who can blame him?

But Abby was true to her word. Last week I received a long letter from her, the contents of which I'm desperate to share with Pete.

I have to choose my time carefully, though, and for now, I keep up the pressure about the bedroom makeover.

"So what about that sale we saw in town?" I say, changing the subject.

Pete copes by refusing to speak of her, though I know he thinks of her every day

convinced it's Abby. I've always been wrong, of course. I still had this image in my head of a teenager with her tongue pierced and her hair strewn with beads.

Did she still wear her hair long, I wondered? Did she still have a penchant for banana milkshakes? Was she happy?

Then, quite out of the blue came a postcard from a town not too far away from us. The message was brief. *I'll be in touch soon. Abby.*

You can imagine – I was ecstatic. At last we knew she was alive and she must be well or she'd have said more, wouldn't she?

Pete stubbornly refused to acknowledge the postcard, I imagine because he thought she'd hurt us again. I magnet-pinned it to the fridge door anyway in the hope that he'd come around.

I've seen him take a sneaky look but he hasn't said anything. Just sighs as if he's expecting

"Okay," he says, resignedly. "If it'll make you happy, Mo, we'll go."

As soon as we walk into the department store, I'm drawn to an

In town, we hit the sales

elegant four-poster bed. Marshmallow-soft pillows appliquéd with vintage lace adorn the white linen bedcovers.

"Wow, imagine sleeping in this," I say.

Pete flips the price tag and whistles through his teeth. "Our car was cheaper!"

"It's an antique," I say, in its defence. But I take another look at the price tag. Even with the sale discount, it's ludicrously expensive. "You're right. Maybe we should have a look around. No point rushing into things."

We soon find a more reasonably priced sprung-edged divan, kick off our shoes and make ourselves comfy.

"This is cosy," I say, regardless of the smiles and nudges of other shoppers. Suddenly, I'm recalling one very special memory. "Abby was born in our first bed. Remember? The one your mother gave us as a wedding gift. It didn't even have a headboard, as I recall."

Other images come rushing back. I was almost a fortnight past my due date. Pete had taken time off work to be with me at the delivery but nothing seemed to be happening. There'd been a couple of false alarms but the baby was in no hurry. Then, one evening, just after supper, the contractions had started.

his head propped on his hand. "I bounded up the stairs two at a time when I heard you yell." He smiles. "There was barely time to phone for an ambulance."

"And before you knew it, you were delivering our first baby."

The smile leaves his lips and a look of concern crosses his face. "I was so scared, Mo."

"So was the midwife. She arrived to find you holding our sleeping daughter wrapped up in a damp tea towel."

I sit up, hugging my knees. "Remember when Abby was a toddler, she used to sneak into our bedroom and snuggle between us?"

Pete gives a long sigh. "She always did come between us, one way or another."

"Pete…"

"Mmm?"

"About Abby… I've heard from her again. She…"

"Mo, can we talk about this some other time?" says Pete, sliding off the bed and getting quickly to his feet. I reach for his hand to stop him but the salesman's hovering over us now and the mood quickly evaporates.

Back home, Pete disappears upstairs. He says he's going to start stripping the

"You may as well spit it out. I presume Abby's got herself in trouble again"

"I'd had so many false starts, I thought I'd got indigestion." I laugh. "Do you remember? I blamed it on your cooking. I'd popped upstairs for a lie down and suddenly everything started happening. You were still downstairs doing the washing-up."

Pete rolls onto his side to look at me,

old wallpaper but I haven't heard any movement. I go up to find him in Abby's old room, clutching the teddy bear she left behind. He looks up at me.

"Go on. You may as well spit it out. I presume Abby's got herself in trouble again," he says. "Is that what you wanted **Continued overleaf…**

to tell me? Are the police involved? I don't think I can bear to hear it, Mo."

"No, no. It's nothing like that." I sit beside him and take the letter out of my pocket. "This came." I hold it out to him but he won't take it.

"I suppose she wants money?"

I press the letter into his hand. "No, she wants to know if she can come home."

I hand it over to him. "What do you say to that?"

Pete takes it from me and it's as if the breath has been knocked out of him. It takes a while for him to compose himself.

"A baby?" he gasps, still gazing at the photograph of the cute little blond fellow. "A boy?"

"He has your eyes, don't you think?"

I press the letter into his hand. "She wants to know if she can come home"

He looks surprised, then his face darkens again. "Been dumped by that yob of hers, has she?"

"No. Just the opposite, actually."

"But you said she wanted to come home."

"For a visit. She has her own home now. Quite a nice place from what she describes. Just a small terrace but it has a garden and…"

"But she's still with him – Bad Whatsisname?" He interrupts.

"Yes. But he's changed. They both have. He goes by his proper name these days. It's Chris. Chris Macintosh. He's a qualified motor mechanic now. Got a steady job, too."

"Chris Macintosh?"

"Which makes our daughter Abby Macintosh," I say.

He nods and then the penny drops. "What? You mean… they're married? Without telling us? When?"

"It doesn't matter when, Pete. They're together and happy. And she has some other news. She's sent me a photograph."

"Does he have a name?"

"Peter. After you. And O'Donnell after my mother. Peter Christopher O'Donnell Macintosh. Sounds rather fine, don't you think?"

I can't read his face this time. He hands back the letter and photograph and goes to the window.

I fear the worst. "Pete, please…"

"I think," he says, turning around with a huge smile on his face, "it's a good job I talked you out of that expensive bed. I hear grandchildren can cost a fortune these days."

A WORD FROM THE AUTHOR

"Whilst watching an interior design programme the phrase 'papering over the cracks' came to mind and it set me thinking about family relationships and how, like a bad makeover, you might wish you'd never participated!"

Fancy That!

Swinging 60s facts that make you go "Wow!"

Family Mix Up

When Dick Van Dyke starred in *Chitty Chitty Bang Bang*, he was a year older than Lionel Jeffries, who played his dad

- **Sales of LPs tripled during the 60s, with 60 million being sold in 1969.**
- James Bond's iconic Aston Martin first appeared in the 1964 film *Goldfinger*.
- **The Whirlpool bath was invented by Roy Jacuzzi in 1968.**

WOW! ● During the mini-skirt craze some dry cleaners charged 2d per inch.

- **The computer mouse was invented by Doug Engelbart in 1965 – 20 years before it was introduced to the public with the Macintosh computer, in 1984.**

Fact!

The Biba brand was founded by Barbara Hulanicki, as a mail order company in 1964

- **Telstar, the first satellite to relay television pictures, was launched in 1962.**
- The first vertical take-off "jump jet", the Harrier, was introduced by Hawker Siddeley Aviation in 1966.

- Domestic smoke alarms were first sold by US company BRK Electronics back in 1967.
- **The industrial robot was invented by the American engineer George Devol in 1961.**

Beetle Drive

During the famous car chase in Steve McQueen's 1968 film *Bullitt*, the cars pass the same VW Beetle four times!

Daisy Chain

It's amazing how a good idea can grow and be added to – and even, sometimes, join up and come full circle!

By Jan Snook

S o – advertise," her husband commented, without looking up from his paper. "What?"

"In a post office window or something," he said. "Or the Parish magazine. You've been going on for weeks about feeling out of place at the mother-and-toddler group…"

"Well I *do*," Sarah interrupted. "They're all so… young. I feel like some old crone always harking back to what it was like when our children were small. I'm the only grandmother there."

"I'd think they'd be interested," her husband said loyally. "I'm sure they're grateful for your experience." He was still looking at the paper, but looked up belatedly. "And you're fifty-four," he added hastily, "which is not – by any stretch of the imagination – an old crone."

His wife regarded him with narrowed eyes. "You could have said that a bit earlier… Anyway," she continued in her normal tone, "it's not as if they're not friendly or anything, it's just that… well, I suppose every generation has to work things out for themselves, that's all. And it did start out as the EWG, so I was

warned. The Ellsbury Wives' Group," Sarah explained, seeing her husband's frown. "Wives, not grandmothers."

"Well you're still a wife, aren't you?"

"You know what I mean."

"You can't be the only one feeling like that," Jim said kindly, looking up at the rueful edge to her voice. "What you need is to find a few other women who look after their grandchildren. There must be lots of them."

And so it began. They concocted an ad, and almost as soon as the notice went in the post office window, Sarah's phone began to ring. There were many more grannies looking after grandchildren than she had realised.

For the first few weeks they met, toddlers in tow, in one another's houses, but in a short time they'd outgrown even the largest of their homes and Sarah found herself arranging to hire Ellsbury Village Hall – the same hall the mother-and-toddler group used – privately sighing with relief that her ornaments

She'd never imagined how many folk were in exactly the same situation…

and carpets were no longer at the mercy of more than twenty energetic toddlers.

But the hall, of course, needed paying for, and a "gaggle of grandmothers", as her husband had so aptly put it, drank a lot of coffee…

She loved looking after her grandchildren

"The trouble is," Sarah said one evening over supper, "that even though we all put in a few pounds, it barely covers the rent, let alone the orange squash and biscuits. And it would be nice to buy a few more toys and equipment. With so many children playing with them, the toys have quite a short shelf life, especially when most of our stuff has come from jumble sales."

"Couldn't you up the price a bit?" Jim asked, helping himself to another potato. "After all, you charge almost nothing, and if the parents were having to pay for child **Continued overleaf…**

Continued from previous page

care at a day nursery or whatever…"

"Money's still very tight in some of the families," Sarah said sadly. "Most of the grans look after their grandchildren because there simply isn't enough money for paid childcare. And because they want to, of course," she added hastily.

high and squeaky and her heart was pounding, but gradually, as she explained about the number of grandparents who regularly took care of their grandchildren, the high cost of childcare, and the needs of the children, she could feel herself relaxing. In no time the presenter was wrapping up

"We've had eight calls with offers of help. You were marvellous, love"

"But there are a couple of single parent families, and quite a few widowed grandmothers in the group. Life's quite a struggle for some of them."

"Couldn't you let those people pay less?"

"Oh Jim, they wouldn't want to accept charity. Think how they'd feel. Perhaps we should do some fundraising. Have a cake sale or something."

"You need a sponsor," Jim replied, as though the matter was settled.

"And how am I supposed to do that?"

It became apparent how she was supposed to do that a few days later. "It's for you," Jim said when the phone rang as she was making scones. "It's the chap from the local radio station."

"What?" Sarah mouthed at him, frowning and wiping her floury hands on her apron, but Jim just handed her the receiver and casually wandered off into the garden.

Two days later, having got up at the crack of dawn and feeling extremely flustered, Sarah found herself in front of a microphone at the radio station.

"So what gave you the idea?" the young man hosting the breakfast show asked, smiling encouragement at her.

Sarah took a deep breath and started, nervously, to speak. Her voice came out

the interview, rattling out the phone number that anyone who was interested should ring, and inviting her to come back in the future and tell them how she'd got on. Sarah left the studio on a cloud. She'd done it. She'd actually talked coherently on the radio to thousands of people without drying up or making a complete fool of herself. If the toddler group made a few pounds as a result, well, the morning would have been well worthwhile. She arrived home still flushed with success.

"I'm not sure that was such a good idea of mine, getting you on that radio show, love," Jim said when she got home.

Sarah's face fell. "Oh dear, was I as

The words were flowing

rubbish as that? I didn't think it had gone too badly." She sounded so doleful that Jim had to hide a smile.

"Well… it could have gone better, I suppose. I mean, since you came off the air an hour ago I've only had… eight phone calls." His face broke into a broad grin. "There've been offers of money, and that toy shop on the High Street rang offering to sponsor you, then the local council rang offering a grant, and a grandfather rang asking whether it was women only and… well, there's a list of all the calls, love." He held out his arms, his eyes shining with pride. "You were marvellous, you really were."

The next few weeks passed in a whirl. Between the toddler group, looking after her grandchildren and dealing with all the letters and phone calls that had continued to come in, she had barely had a minute to herself. The group had almost doubled in size since the radio broadcast, and they were now meeting three days a week. Several grandfathers had arrived, and a woman had appeared one morning at the hall, with two-year-old twins and her Polish mother-in-law in tow. The grandmother spoke barely a word of woman who was pouring juice into assorted beakers. The hall was full of noisy children: the grandfathers were a bit more relaxed about the normal rough-and-tumble of small boys, and the toddler group was the better for it, Sarah admitted to herself as she saw her own grandson charging recklessly across the hall on a tricycle.

There was a tug at her skirt, and Sarah looked down at a very small girl, whose mouth was moving inaudibly over the noise. Sarah bent down to her level and put an arm round her. "Lay-dee, lay-dee," the little voice said in her ear. "Lay-dee, over dair." The child ran off and Sarah stood up and walked over to the woman whom she recognised as the one who ran the mother-and-toddler group she used to attend. The woman's eyes were round with wonder.

"My goodness," she said. "I heard you on the radio, and I just came to see how you were getting on." She stared at all the activities in progress, then laughed. "Actually, I was wondering whether you'd like to use some of our toys since you meet on different days, but you're far better equipped than we are, so I'm sure you don't need to." She looked as though she was about to say something else, but hesitated.

The young mum looked embarrassed. "Actually, I came to apologise…"

English and had looked terrified.

That had all been several weeks ago. Sarah looked about her and smiled. She was mixing paint for a throng of budding artists while another grandmother threaded their unwilling arms into very necessary overalls. The Polish lady was laying out coffee cups on a tray and chatting in rapidly improving English to a

"Would you like a cup of coffee?" Sarah asked. "It's Anne, isn't it? We're just about to stop and have a drink."

"Actually I would," Anne said gratefully. "I really came to apologise."

"Whatever for?" Sarah asked in surprise.

"Well, on the radio you said…" the young mother bit her lip, then carried on

Continued overleaf…

in a rush. "You said you'd felt out of place with all of us."

"I may have done," Sarah answered slowly, "but I only meant because I was so much older…"

"No, we should have been more welcoming," Anne said firmly. "And I'm sorry." She took the proffered cup of coffee and looked around again. "Though the studio. "It's really turned into more of a community group than a toddler group. We've teamed up with the group I used to belong to – the mothers-and-toddlers – because although we oldies have more time and experience, the young ones have a lot more energy! Then a few grandfathers joined in, and that encouraged some of the young fathers to come along when they

"We've decided it would be better if the group wasn't exclusively anything"

this looks wonderful." She paused and took a sip of coffee. "I was also going to tell you that we've missed you." Sarah put up her hands to object, but Anne continued.

"No, really. Several times people have mentioned that if only you were there we could have asked you. Lots of people don't have their mothers nearby, and you gave us lots of ideas for coping with everyday problems. You made it all sound so… so *easy*."

"Well I did have four children of my own," Sarah said. "You're bound to pick up a few tips along the way. And there are times when I've missed you, too," she began, but a small boy chose that moment to fall off his scooter and was howling at the other side of the hall. "Like now," she said to Anne's retreating back as she flew, far faster than anyone else in the room could, to pick him up.

And listeners will remember Sarah, the glamorous gran who started up a toddler group especially for oldies," the radio presenter was saying jovially. "So tell us, Sarah, how's it been going?"

"Well, we've learned a lot," Sarah said, smiling and feeling a good deal more confident than the last time she'd been in have a chance. My own husband's been a few times, too – which hadn't happened before," she added laughing. "Everyone's got something to contribute."

"So you'll be changing the name of the group, will you? What are you now, The Three Generations?"

"Well we were thinking of something like that, but only this week we were joined by a remarkable great-grandmother, which is wonderful," Sarah said, her enthusiasm coming over the radio waves loud and clear.

"We've decided it's no good being exclusively for grandmothers, or exclusively young mums, or exclusively anything, so we're keeping the original name. The EWG. It used to be the Ellsbury Wives Group. Only now it stands for the Everybody's-Welcome-Group. And they really are."

A WORD FROM THE AUTHOR

"I was inspired to write this when I saw a grandmother's ad in a Post Office window – which coincided with the arrival of our beautiful new grandson!"

Teatime Treat

LIGHT FLAKY PASTRY

Mini Berry Mille Feuilles

EASY FRUIT FILLINGS

Ingredients

- 225g (8oz) all-butter ready-made puff pastry
- 1 medium egg white, beaten
- 1tbsp caster sugar
- 6 medium-sized strawberries, washed and hulled
- 150ml (½pt) double cream
- 3tbsp strawberry jam

**Preparation time:
25mins plus cooling
Cooking time: 15mins
Makes: 6**

● Preheat the oven to 220°C, Fan Oven 200°C, Gas Mark 7. Line a baking tray with baking parchment. On a lightly floured surface, roll out the **pastry** to make a rectangle approx. 25x23cm (10x9in).

● Carefully transfer the pastry to the tray and prick all over with a fork. Brush lightly with **egg white** and sprinkle evenly with the **sugar**. Bake in the oven for 12-15mins until golden and risen. Allow to cool on the tray.

● Carefully transfer the pastry to a board and using a large sharp knife, cut in half lengthways, and then cut each half into 6 equal slices.

● When you are ready to serve your guests, thinly slice the **strawberries** and lightly whip the **cream**. Sandwich 2 pieces of pastry together, both sugar side up, with whipped cream, sliced strawberries and a little **jam**. Serve immediately.

FOOD STYLING: KATHRYN HAWKINS. PHOTOGRAPHY: LIGHTHOUSE

Toll Story

Will Anne find life in the fast lane in this motorway romance?

By Douglas McPherson

The training didn't take long. "You put your hand out. You take their pound. You press the green button to open the barrier. Shouldn't be too much trouble for a girl with your education!"

Evie, the supervisor, let out a cackle and Anne cursed herself for putting her art degree on the application form.

Working in a motorway bridge toll booth was hardly Anne's dream job. But it was a job – which she undeniably needed now Darren was gone. At least it got her out of the house – even if it was at five o'clock in the morning.

As a child she'd quite fancied a job with from handling 360 coins an hour.

By the end of her shift she wanted nothing more than a long, semi-comatose soak in the tub to wash off the eau-du-exhaust fumes that clung to her like a second, oily skin and rendered her hair completely lifeless.

She certainly didn't have the energy to paint – which she needed to do if she were ever to get a job more worthy of her talents. She barely had the strength to microwave her dinner before another early night and the far-too-soon ringing of her alarm clock.

Hand out. Take the pound. Press the… Hang on. To her surprise, instead of a pound, someone had handed her a

She could scarcely have felt less glamorous than she did in her current work wear

a uniform. A nurse, perhaps, if she could bear the sight of blood. Maybe she would have met a nice doctor.

Or an air hostess – like the glamour puss Darren ran off with.

She could scarcely have felt less glamorous than she did in her current work wear: a stiff and shiny high-visibility waterproof over a bulky black fleece that was definitely necessary in a draughty toll booth before the sun came up.

Hand out. Take the pound. Press the green button.

Anne's palm was as black as a miner's

single, brightly wrapped chocolate.

She looked down and met the clear blue eyes of a man about her age in a bright red sports car.

With a sheepish look, he held up his pound and patted a rather cuddly belly.

"I shouldn't eat them all myself," he said. "And, well, you looked like you needed something to cheer you up."

A moment before, it would have taken a lot more than a sweet to cheer Anne up. But something about the man's obvious sincerity made her forget how much her bones ached from standing so long in the chill wind of the estuary.

"Thanks," she said, and to her own surprise, found herself smiling back as he beamed up at her like a big, friendly puppy.

Hand out. Take the pound. Press the green button.

The next day it was a hazelnut crunch and a "Hear it's going to be sunnier later."

The day after, it was a strawberry centre, then, "Do you have a favourite, by the way?"

"Well, I like the ones with Brazil nuts."

"Hold on, then."

Oblivious to the queue of cars behind him, he upended his box on to the black leather passenger seat and rummaged around among the brightly wrapped sweets before declaring triumphantly, "Here we are! Just for you!"

Continued overleaf...

Continued from previous page

Tired as she was, Anne was almost disappointed when the weekend came and she knew she wouldn't see the man with the sweets for two whole days.

She knew she was being silly, but his daily presents and sweeter smiles actually made her look forward to going to work.

She wondered where he went when he drove off up the ramp to the bridge, and what he did all day. She wondered whether he had anyone to go home to when he drove back the other way.

Don't even think about it, she told herself. As if a man like that would have anything in common with someone who worked in a toll booth.

On Saturday, though, she got her hair done. And on Sunday she got her paints out for the first time in ages.

Hand out. Take the –

In his outstretched hand was a whole box of the ones with the Brazil nuts in.

"Don't eat them all at once." He grinned. "I'm going away for a few days, so they've got to last you."

"Well, here's a going away present," said Anne, and handed him a watercolour of a man smiling up from the seat of a bright red sports car.

Hand out. Take the pound. Press the green button.

Darren had never liked her paintings. He'd scoffed at her burning ambition of being an illustrator.

Darren wanted a woman who cooked, cleaned and had babies. When they hadn't

arrived, he'd blamed her – although he was the one who refused to get checked out.

Perhaps that was why he needed his trolley dolly, Anne guessed – to prove something.

Hand out. Take the pound. Press the green button.

"I thought you said you were going away."

"I am, later. But I wanted to thank you properly for that wonderful painting. How about over dinner, at the weekend, when I get back?"

Hand out. Take the pound. Press the green button.

The rest of the week was sheer torture. Why hadn't she said yes? It was the moment she'd dreamed of. But when it came, the reality was just too scary.

That car. That posh accent. Those soft fingers against her palm. He was probably a surgeon. Or a professor at the university.

As Darren had always told her, "People like that live in a different world. You might kid yourself with your fancy degree but to them you'll always be the same as me – down 'ere, while they're up there."

It was better to get real now, she decided, than get hurt later.

But would she ever forget the look in his big, vulnerable eyes as hope crumbled to disappointment?

Hand out. Take the pound. Press the green button.

Monday came, and as the clock ticked towards his usual time, Anne couldn't stop herself scanning the stream of cars fanning out across the road towards the line of toll booths.

When she saw the red sports car, she felt her stomach tighten and wondered if he'd choose a different lane. But no. He was coming her way as usual.

Hand out. Take the pound. Press the green button.

He was two cars away. She hoped her eyes weren't too red, and wished she'd put on some make-up.

Hand out. Take the pound. Press the green button.

He handed her a piece of paper and gave her a sheepish grin.

"I'm afraid I'm not in your league as an artist, but I am persistent."

Anne looked at the sheet of paper. On it was a drawing of a man on his knees in

"That was the best evening I've ever had. Please say you're free again tonight?"

"I'd love to be, but can we make it the weekend? I'm so tired after work."

Hand out. Take the pound. Press the green button.

"Is it still two days to the weekend?"

"I know," said Anne. "It's awful, isn't it?"

Hand out. Take the – earrings?

"You forgot these." He grinned, and she shared his blush.

Hand out. Take the –

In his hand was a velvet ring box, open to show the glint of diamonds.

"I was going to ask you last night," he said with that sheepish smile she adored. "But here seemed more appropriate."

He grinned. "I'm afraid I'm not in your league as an artist, but I am persistent"

front of a toll booth, his hands clasped in the manner of prayer.

At the top was a heart-shaped speech bubble in which he'd written, "Reconsider dinner?" At the bottom was a mobile phone number.

Hand out. Take the pound. Press –

Anne should have known it would happen eventually. Darren's work took him all over. Even so, it was a shock to see his builder's van pull up to her toll booth. Darren was as shocked as she was.

"What are you doing here?"

"I would have thought that was obvious," Anne said through gritted teeth.

"Look, Anne," Darren said awkwardly, "I really don't know what to say."

"Try goodbye," said Anne, and pressed the button that lifted the barrier.

Hand out. Take the –

– bunch of red roses.

"It's beautiful," said Anne. "But you know it's your money I really want, don't you?"

For a moment he looked confused. Then he grinned and dug into his pocket.

For the final time, Anne put her hand out, took the pound and pressed the button that raised the barrier. Then she threw off her shiny high-visibility coat, ran out of the toll booth and jumped into the passenger seat of the red car.

He put his foot down and they drove up the ramp of the bridge into the rising sun of a brand new day.

A WORD FROM THE AUTHOR

"I've always admired the stoicism of the men and women taking our pounds in motorway toll booths. Perhaps we should all start giving them presents."

ILLUSTRATIONS: JIM DEWAR, PHOTOLIBRARY, MEDIABLITZ IMAGES

Those Were The Days

She was simply not interested in finding a man. And now there was a war on, her views on that were even firmer!

By Alison Carter

There's far, far too much to do," Gillian told her mother flatly. "It's too late, anyway – I'm thirty-two, for goodness' sake."

Her mother smiled. "Well, that's your choice, Gilly. I have three lovely grandchildren already. Though I will say that a pretty girl like you could –"

"Mum!" Gill spoke sharply. "I'm not a girl any more, and I'm not… well, that's Jean's department."

She tipped a pile of vegetable peelings into the garden bin. "Anyway, I'm going up to bed. I start my early shift at five."

days a 'girl' can have much more to her life than finding a husband."

Gill had not been in the ATS long. In their Lancashire coastal town, the ATS worked on the anti-aircraft guns. Gill felt lucky. So many women in the Service just scrubbed parsnips for mess halls or cleaned lavatories.

Proudly wearing a new uniform on her first day, Gill had told Jean and their mother about her duties.

"I'll be tracking German planes. I'll fuse the shells, and –"

"You'll do what?" Jean shifted the baby on her hip and stared.

"Fuse the shells. It's…" Gill looked

She felt lucky to be working on the guns. So many women just cleaned lavatories

"You do take life very seriously," her mother observed gently.

"I have every reason to."

"Jack was a long time ago, dear…"

Gilly sighed. "And I'm supposed to forgive the lying cad, cheer up just like that, and go out on the town?"

"Well, no, but –"

"To tell you the truth, Mum, I'm not even heartbroken any more. Not really. I've just found other things to do. These

impatient. "Well, I'm not sure what it is yet. No actual shooting, though."

"That's a relief," her mother said.

"I don't think it's a relief," Gill retorted. "I'm willing to serve my country in any way I possibly can."

One July day in 1940, Gill walked into the battery and peeled off her jacket.

"Goodness, it's hot. What are you two crack personnel doing?"

It was hard work, but Gill was glad to be busy

Diane idly polished a piece of sighting apparatus. "Looking out for Stukas."

"Well, you're facing the wrong way," Gill remarked dryly.

Diane heaved her chair round, scowling.

Gill hung up her jacket. "Mr Churchill is changing the name of the LDV. It was on the wireless."

"I don't blame him," Eliza said. "My dad says if you ask for Local Defence Volunteers and then don't arm them, what do you expect but that every wag will call them 'Look, Duck, Vanish'?"

Diane giggled. "LDV. Priceless. Do you know that they only got army-issue armbands to start with, poor things? Not a weapon amongst them."

Continued overleaf…

"That's all right," Eliza said brightly. "Haven't they all still got their bayonets from the trenches?"

Gill frowned. "Don't be flippant. Now it's the Home Guard, and an important organisation it is, too."

The other two looked at her with a mixture of affection and amusement.

"Solemn old Gilly," said Eliza.

"Oh, oh!" Diana jumped up. "How could I forget? There's a dance, or at least a social – Friday night at seven at Prether Village Hall. All in uniform are invited."

Unusually, Gill decided to go to the social. She'd keep an eye on the other ATS girls. Gill saw herself in the role of chaperone, at times.

She ironed the only reasonable dress in her neglected wardrobe, and met the girls on the way.

Diane stopped outside the hall to smooth her skirt. "It's a shame there's such a lack of men," she said, "because you, Gillian Openshaw, look very nice."

Gill laughed. "You sound surprised."

"She's right, though," Eliza said. "You do look a treat."

"Don't be ridiculous," answered Gill.

Later, once inside, Gill was at the tea urn when she scalded her hand. "Oh, for heaven's sake!" she yelped in pain.

"Cold water," announced a low male voice behind her. Its owner firmly took her arm and led her to the kitchen. Wordlessly, he held her hand under running water.

"It'll be fine," he said, almost to himself. His head turned for the first time from his task and he saw her surprised expression.

"Railwayman," he commented, as if in explanation. "Prether Station."

Gill noticed the fine creases around his eyes as he smiled.

"It happens to me all the time," he added. "With the steam."

"Oh, of course." Gill's hand dripped into the sink. "Thanks."

"Philip Glenn. Pleased to meet you."

Gill gave her name and they returned to the hall. There wasn't much space so they stood a little awkwardly side by side, watching the dancers.

Gill was relieved he didn't ask for a dance. Dancing wasn't her thing. The railwayman looked to be in his early forties, so too old for the call-up. But of course if he was on the railways, then he couldn't be spared to fight anyway.

"Reserved occupation," she said aloud, almost to herself. He turned.

"I'm in the LDV as well," he said defensively, "for what it's worth."

"It's worth a great deal," Gill assured him earnestly. "But aren't you the Home Guard these days?"

He laughed. "Yes. How could I forget? Some card will find a new nickname for us soon, though. Everyone's a comic when there's a war on."

"I'm not," Gill replied. Then she blushed. *Serious old Gilly again.* "I mean, I can never remember a single joke that's told to me."

"Nor can I. When I was a kid I used to ink them on my hand. You can imagine how bad I was then at the delivery."

Gill found herself laughing. It felt good.

The following Monday her section was assigned a series of munitions inspections. Gill felt proud of the new privilege. But she noticed that the scald still hurt. It got in the way. It reminded her of that social, and that man.

Her mother announced she had to visit a sick aunt at the weekend.

"Poor Aunt Reenie," Gill said. "I'll come along too, shall I?"

"But it's your day off."

Gill shrugged casually. "Oh, I like the train. And Reenie, too."

Her mother looked astonished. "I don't remember you saying so before."

When she saw Philip Glenn through the dusty window of the station office, and he waved at her, Gill said to her mother lightly, "What an odd coincidence. I met that man last week."

Her mother was struggling with a basket. "That's nice," she said vaguely.

Mr Glenn came out of the office, wiping his hands on his overalls.

"How's the hand?" he asked.

"Pardon?" Gill felt hot. "Warm, isn't it?"

I'm supposed to be the man in charge of an entire railway station." He stood up. "I mean," he said haltingly, "if you are Mrs Openshaw. I met your daughter recently, but of course your name would be different from her married name so –"

"We're both Openshaw." Gill's mother eyed the tall man in front of her. "I'm sure I don't know why we've all become so interested in names. My daughter here claims a new interest in railways."

Gill blushed and looked down.

"I understand that," Mr Glenn said. "I'm an enthusiast myself." He swallowed. "Actually, my friends say I'm married to the railway." There was a pause. "Rather than being actually, um, married, or…" His voice faltered.

Mrs Openshaw peered at him. "I don't know what you're on about," she remarked, "but if this is the ten-fourteen, we've to be on it."

Gill was leaving the ATS base one Friday evening when Philip Glenn appeared wearing his Home Guard

She'd never noticed before how good-looking the Home Guard uniform was…

"It is July," he said gently. "Your hand?"

"Oh, of course!" Gill's arm flew up, knocking her mother's elbow. "It's improving, thank you."

"I'm glad about that," he said.

There was a pause, during which both of them noticed her mother scrabbling for packages. They dived to the floor, knocking their heads together.

"For goodness' sake, Gilly!" her mother exclaimed, embarrassed.

"My fault," Philip Glenn said, on his knees. "Stupid of me, Mrs Openshaw, and

uniform. She'd seen the uniform often, but somehow had not noticed before how good-looking it was.

"I was passing, and saw you come out," he said lightly. "It's a glorious evening."

They fell into step. She tried to think of something else to talk about other than her blessed hand.

"The Home Guard," she said. "They have such potential."

He chuckled. "To keep us off the streets, you mean?"

Continued overleaf…

Continued from previous page

"I beg your pardon?"

"You must have heard about all the private armies that were forming, ready for any invasion."

Gill stopped. "I'm sure it wasn't like –"

"Reg Godber, the plumber on Barratt Street, he'd practically formed a regiment."

"Good heavens." Gill walked on. "That would be foolish."

"You have to see the funny side," he said.

"Oh, yes, of course you do," said Gill.

Weeks passed. Gill met Philip Glenn surprisingly often. He often had work to do in her neighbourhood. He talked about having a sister-in-law living nearby, but didn't specify the address.

She went on frequent walks herself, for a change of scene. So many routes seemed to pass near the station.

"Have you noticed how the railway station is always the beating heart of a town?" she commented to Mother.

Philip was sort of a friend anyway, by now. "And exercise is terribly important," Gill said sagely, "in the Services."

Phillip's face was near hers, his breath warm on her cheek in the chilly air

She began to speculate that if it were peacetime, she might be doing whatever women do to get a man's attention. In peacetime, if she were younger, if she were beautiful, if they lived in another universe, she would get new lipstick or get Jean to do her hair. In peacetime even a woman like her, a practical woman, might fall in love. But they weren't at peace, and there was work to do.

How's your Mr Glenn?" Jean asked. The winter had set in, and Gill had taken out her coat and found it badly worn. How long could she go for walks wearing that, once the weather worsened? The winds off the sea were cutting.

"He's not *my* Mr Glenn."

"All right." The corner of Jean's mouth bent upwards. "You are funny, Gilly."

"Funny? How do you mean?"

"I hope he's not like you. Nobody'll get anywhere if he is."

Gill scowled. "I've no idea what you're talking about."

"You're hopeless," Jean said lightly as she opened the door to the hall.

"I am not –" But the door had closed. Gill shrugged. She was certainly not hopeless. She'd recently been selected for car maintenance training.

Gill grew to hate her stupid old coat. It wasn't that it was old-fashioned and made her look shapeless; of course that sort of thing wasn't important. But it didn't do its job. She was trying to wrap it closer about her at the bus stop when Philip Glenn walked out of the tobacconist's.

"Hello," he said, hurrying towards her. "You look frozen." He removed his jacket as he approached and draped in over her.

"I'm fine. The number six will be along soon. I can't take your –"

"I'm like a gas boiler," he interrupted. "I generate my own heat." He was wrapping the jacket around her as he spoke, doing up the top button, standing very close.

"Gillian." He was looking at her.

"Thanks, then." She looked along the street for the bus. "Well, we've finished the motors course. That oil! Diane whined the whole week about getting it under her nails." Her words were tumbling out.

Philip's face was near hers, the warmth of

So many paths led to the station

his breath on her cheek. "Honestly, those girls!" She knew that he was going to put his arms around her. "My bus is late," she rattled on. "They ought to lay on more –"

He kissed her. There was nothing she could do to escape. He had hold of her jacket – his jacket.

Afterwards she stared at him in panic. "I'll just walk back instead…"

Emotions fought each other, all in a jumbled instant. It had been fine, their friendship, but now he had kissed her. That wasn't what she intended. It wasn't the plan, surely. She was Gillian Openshaw; useful in a crisis, capable, a pal.

"Gillian." His voice was different. "Gill. Don't go. Please."

"I can return the jacket when, er…" She pulled it off. The scratchy wool irritated her neck. Cold air struck her throat. "I'll be off then." She looked at the ground.

"I'm sorry," he said, letting go. She could breathe again. "I decided that if I didn't at least try… if I didn't say something, then –"

"I have to go home. Now." Gill looked frantically at her watch. "I'm in early tomorrow, you see."

"The bus will be faster," he said lamely, the rejected jacket now clutched limply against his side.

"But the bus isn't here." She wanted to cry. Everything was wrong. She turned and walked off determinedly, concentrating on the hard tap of her shoe leather on the pavement, trying not to think about him standing there.

It didn't take Gill more than half a mile to know how stupid she was. The wind beat her hair into a tangle and she tugged it back angrily. What had she run from? The love of a man whom she thought about every waking moment? She was nearly thirty-three years old and didn't understand her own feelings.

Gill Openshaw threw herself into work. Hadn't that been her intention anyway? She volunteered for endless armaments inspections, trying not to feel grateful that her country was at war and so had plenty for her – a spinster – to do.

It proved impossible to avoid Philip Glenn. She stepped warily off a train from St Helens one cold day and he was **Continued overleaf…**

hurrying along the platform. He virtually ran into her, and stepped back two paces.

"Miss Openshaw. How nice to see you again. How is your mother?" His dark eyes held hers.

"Oh! Well, thank you." Gill was taken by surprise. She had planned what she would say, how to apologise – how, somehow, to let him know that…

"Look," he began. "I'm really sorry. Perhaps I overstepped –"

"I'm sorry," she blurted out, interrupting him quickly, yet stumbling over the words.

There was a silence between them, while the train pulled out noisily. Smoke hurtled past them. She coughed, and it broke the silence.

He nodded his head briefly and turned away. Gill's heart turned cold. She'd said that word wrongly. *Sorry.* She'd suggested by it that she was sorry, but she could never accept his love. That wasn't what it was, not at all.

Philip was moving away, talking to a guard. Her embarrassment, her stupidity, had driven him away again.

Soon afterwards, Gill entered the grocer in Main Street and glimpsed, in the dim light, a well-known profile moving back into the shadows. Such a profile!

The grocer hesitated, wondering whom to serve first. Gill turned to the high-banked shelves and pretended to examine the tins of condensed milk. She knew she looked ridiculous, like a Martian with no experience of Earthly foodstuffs.

Clutching a ration book, her hand shook. Embarrassment – stupid, childish awkwardness – kept her from turning and speaking to him.

He left the shop, and she knew that that was how they were destined to meet. She had rejected him, and he believed – was

"I wish I could get it right a second time"

now doubtless certain – that she would not be changing her mind.

In April, 1941, Gill's CO circulated a request for women to train for basic carpentry at the Town Hall. She was glad women were taking on more and more "men's" tasks; now she could hammer and bang, forgetting her unhappiness.

She pushed open the hall's heavy door. Philip Glenn was standing at the front, talking to an army officer. The sight of him, the smile, the way the corners of his eyes creased – it drove the breath from her. She steadied herself, fixing her eyes on the benches erected around the hall.

"Mr Trent," she said with forced cheerfulness, accepting a canvas apron from a small man who'd approached, a family friend. "Didn't know you'd be here."

"Just lending a hand. Philip's the man for wood. Man of many talents. Do you know Philip Glenn?"

Gill stared at the tools in front of her. Other women chatted happily. She got through the first half hour, and then he approached her bench.

"Good morning." His tone was steady but he fiddled with a shaving.

"So you two have met after all?" Mr Trent bustled up. "Gill's done a decent job with a mortice and tenon here."

"It's a mess," Gill said. She laid a protective hand over her work.

"Nonsense! You've managed very well to…" Mr Trent's voice faded away when he saw Gill's bowed head and flushed cheeks. He sensed that he wasn't wanted.

"Careful, Mrs Bancroft," he called

Their fingers touched. An electric shock passed through her.

"Mr Trent," he said loudly, but still looking at Gill.

Mr Trent hurried over. "Section Commander Glenn?"

"Miss Openshaw here needs some air. Will you take charge, please?"

They walked together out of the hall, across the scrub and the lane to the dunes. It was cold in the winter wind.

"So, there's something," he said, "that you'd like to take another run at?"

A smile began to play round her mouth. "Yes. A… a scene."

"It's a fair old way to the bus stop."

However disastrous the outcome may be, she knew she had to speak now…

cheerfully, moving away, "you'll have somebody's eye out with that."

Philip remained quite still.

"You can remake the joint," he said quietly. "We all make mistakes."

"Bad mistakes," she answered. Her heart was pounding.

There was a silence that seemed endless. Chisels scraped around them.

She had to speak now, whatever the disastrous, humiliating outcome might be, or regret it for the rest of her life.

"Do you ever think," she said, her voice low, "that you'd like to go back and remake something?"

"No," he said slowly. "Because I usually know what I want."

He stopped. Gill had lifted her face to look at him, full of emotion.

"Well," she said in a whisper, "sometimes I wish that I could get it right a second time."

He slid the wood from under her hand.

"The beach will do just fine," she said.

"But this time, when I speak to you, you won't vanish?"

Gill laughed. "Or duck."

He looked puzzled.

"Look, duck, vanish…" Gill said softly. "How silly of me to think of the LDV at a moment like this."

"No ducking, no vanishing," he said slowly, putting his arms around her.

"No. Can I borrow your jacket again?" she asked him coyly.

"Only if I can kiss you again."

"It's a bargain."

A WORD FROM THE AUTHOR

"I was reading about the Home Guard, and imagining a man left at home while others went to fight. Naturally, I wanted a romance for him!"

Turn Back Time

When there's nowhere to go, the right path can present itself in the strangest way…

By Teresa Ashby

Claire muttered and dropped the sheet she was about to hang on the line back into the laundry basket. "What now? This had better not be another of your false alarms, Dusty."

The little dog stopped barking for a moment and looked up at her, feathery ears upright, bright eyes full of mischief.

She hesitated. What if it was Tony? But of course it wouldn't be. She'd told him in no uncertain terms what would happen if he dared come back.

So why did she spend all day every day wishing he would?

Dusty raced ahead into the house, talking about. Was this some long lost cousin she'd never heard of? Or was she the one Tony had been seeing?

Claire had heard of things like that happening. Girlfriends turning up on the doorstep, throwing lives into chaos. Not that things could be much worse. They'd split up and were living apart. How much worse could it get?

"I couldn't help but notice you didn't have a sign up," the girl went on. "You used to have one propped up in the bay window. Every year Mum would point to it as we came up the path and say, 'No Vacancies, that's because we're staying.' It was long ago but…"

"Vacancies?" Claire said. She was more concerned with the fact that the

Claire was more concerned that the girl seemed almost on the verge of tears

skidding down the hall and hurling herself at the front door.

Claire told Dusty to hold back and opened the door to a young woman who was smiling all over her face.

"I'm really sorry for just turning up like this, but I couldn't find your number, and the old number I had didn't work. I would have written, but I only decided to do this last night and…"

Claire didn't have a clue what she was girl had gone from smiling to smiling desperately. She seemed to be on the verge of either laughter or tears.

"You are still a B&B, aren't you?"

"I'm sorry," Claire shook her head. "We bought this house about five years ago. I wasn't aware it was ever a B&B."

Now she was suspicious. What if this was one of those doorstep scams you were always reading about in the paper? What if while she was chatting to this

Claire found herself inviting the girl in for coffee

young woman, her accomplice had come in the back door and was nipping out with all her valuables. Not that she had any. She'd already lost what was most valuable to her. Or maybe she'd thrown it away.

"I'm so sorry," the young woman said. "I didn't think to check. How stupid."

"Well, I'm sure you'll find somewhere to stay," Claire said cheerfully, whilst trying to ignore the fact that her visitor looked close to tears.

She thought of all the things she had to do – bake a cake for her niece's birthday, finish hanging out the **Continued overleaf…**

washing, shopping, ironing, making an appointment with the solicitor which she had somehow not got round to doing – the list was endless, as always.

"Have you come far?"

The girl nodded, biting her lip nervously.

"What's your name?"

"Helen."

"Why don't you come in, Helen? I was just about to put the kettle on. And don't mind Dusty, her bark is worse than her bite. I can make a couple of calls and see if I can find a B&B nearby for you."

Helen's shoulders sagged.

"That's so kind, but this is about more than finding somewhere to stay the night," she said.

"Come in nevertheless

Her gaze strayed to the window where she saw the sparkling sea

"You can't turn back time, can you, no matter how much you might want to?"

and tell me about it," Claire said.

"I suppose I'm being silly," Helen said as she fondled Dusty's now relaxed and floppy ears while Claire made coffee. "You can't turn back time, can you, no matter how much you might want to?"

Claire couldn't agree more. If only she could turn back time. A year or so should do the trick. Even a few weeks…

She'd do anything to take back what she'd said. But when the factory closed last year and she lost her job as supervisor, her confidence went with it.

She was bad tempered and always moaning at Tony. One day he'd come home late and said he'd gone for a drink with a girl from work. Claire had been numb with shock.

"I just needed to spend some time with someone happy," he'd said. "It didn't mean anything."

"Happy?" she'd screamed. "How can you expect me to be happy? I can't get a job and we could lose this house."

"Why don't you stop feeling sorry for yourself and do something about it?"

Eventually he'd shouted that she wasn't the girl he'd married and she shouted back that in that case he should sling his hook.

"Right, I will," he'd said, not moving. So she'd pushed him, actually shoved him towards the door.

"Go on then, what are you waiting for? Go! I don't want you here any more. I hate you!"

She shuddered when she thought of those last words. She didn't hate him. Nothing could be further from the truth, but once the words were out and the hurt was raw in his eyes, there was no going back.

> **"Go on – I don't want you here any more!" She shuddered at those last words**

"Right," he'd said. "I'll go."

He'd gone upstairs to pack while she'd sat trembling in the kitchen, thinking that any minute he'd walk back in the door and they'd make up. But he'd come down the stairs with his bags and his last act had been to slam his keys on the hall table.

"Goodbye, Claire," he'd said, his eyes as hard as granite.

"Don't come back," she'd hissed even though what she really wanted to do was apologise and beg him to stay.

"Are you all right?" Helen asked. Claire shook herself back to the present and poured the coffee.

"I'm fine," she said brightly. "Now tell me why it's so important to you that you stay here."

Helen smiled. "We used to come here every year in the summer holidays, until I was thirteen. The two or three weeks we spent here every year were the happiest of my life."

"Why did you stop coming?"

Helen lowered her eyes and fiddled with the handle of her mug.

"My parents split up," she said. "Dad moved in with someone else. It didn't work out, but Mum wouldn't have him back. We couldn't afford holidays after that. We used to spend a few days with Mum's sister in Brighton, but it just wasn't the same without Dad."

"I'm so sorry," Claire said, thinking at least she and Tony hadn't got round to starting a family yet, so there were no children to suffer the anguish of their break up.

"It was a long time ago," Helen said with a weak smile. "Over the years Mum and Dad have been forced to meet up at weddings and Christenings, even funerals. They've always been polite and distant, even when their grandchildren started to arrive. But a year ago my older sister had a premature baby. She was so tiny and frail – like a little red featherless bird."

Claire already had a lump in her throat just listening. She simply nodded at Helen to go on.

"It was a long, uphill battle," Claire said. "Little Amelia was in hospital for months and there were constant setbacks and infections and calls in the middle of the night. Sometimes it looked as if she wouldn't make it. But in the end she came home and she's absolutely fine now."

Helen smiled warmly and suddenly dipped into her bag and found an envelope with a handful of photos
Continued overleaf…

which she passed over to Claire.

"The first one was taken just after she was born. You can see how fragile she was. And yet look at her now!"

"She's gorgeous," Claire said.

"Indeed she is," Helen sighed. "Mum and Dad were always meeting at the hospital and one day when things looked particularly bleak, Dad put his arm round her and she cried against his shoulder. It was the last thing on my

"I don't have a family," Claire said. "It's just me."

They had been planning to fill the house with children one day. Well that wasn't going to happen now, was it?

She wouldn't be able to keep the house much longer anyway. How would she afford it? She couldn't expect Tony to go on paying the mortgage for ever and there was no realistic chance of another job for her in the near future,

Claire straightened up. He was right — she had to stop feeling sorry for herself

mind at the time, but looking back I think part of me knew they still loved each other. The way she turned to him and the way he held her."

Helen's gaze strayed to the kitchen window from where she could see the sea with the sun sparkling on the waves.

"They're always looking for excuses to bump into each other. I thought if I booked them a few days here it would be the extra little push that they need."

"That certainly does sound quite romantic," Claire said.

"You think so? It's been suggested that we send them to Paris or somewhere like that, but they both get so stressed by travelling and I think what they need is somewhere to chill out. Somewhere that's familiar, but still away from everyone."

"They can stay here," Claire said.

It would give her something to do with her time so she didn't spend all day, every day wondering where Tony was, who he was with now and how stupid she'd been.

"That would be wonderful, but what about your family?"

not now that the factory had gone.

She straightened up. Tony was right. She had to stop feeling sorry for herself.

"When would they like to come?"

"It would have been their thirtieth wedding anniversary next weekend… is that too soon?"

Claire was pleased. It meant she wouldn't have time to rethink her hasty decision to have them stay.

"Next weekend would be just great."

"I'll pay the going rate of course," Helen said.

"Oh, but I couldn't… I mean I'm not even a proper B&B."

"Perhaps you should be," Helen said. "The location is perfect and it's such a happy house. It has a wonderful atmosphere. If spending the weekend here doesn't bring my parents back together, I don't know what will."

For the next few days Claire worked at getting two rooms ready, giving them a good clean, washing the curtains and putting flowers on the window sills.

The day before Joyce and Trevor were due to arrive there was a knock on the door. Helen rushed to answer it worried that her guests were arriving early and when she found Tony on the doorstep, her heart hammered against her ribs so hard it took her breath away.

"Hi," he said with an uncertain smile. "I was just…"

A furry blur shot down the hall, barking and shrieking. Dusty leapt up at Tony and he caught her in his arms. She squirmed and wriggled, licking madly at his face.

"I've missed you too," he said, almost laughing.

"What do you want?" Claire said.

"I think I may have left my good shoes under the bed," he said. He only wore his good shoes for special occasions. "I have an appointment in town," he went on.

That would be with the solicitor, Claire thought gloomily. She let him in and he hurried upstairs and came back with a shoe box under his arm.

"I'm expecting someone," she said.

"Estate agent I suppose," he said. She went cold.

"Goodbye, Tony," she snapped, closing the door behind him.

He only came back for his good shoes

When Joyce and Trevor arrived the next day they were holding hands. So Helen was right – the spark was still there.

"We couldn't believe it when Helen told us she'd booked us in here," Joyce enthused. "We had such happy times here," Trevor added with a big smile.

Watching them together made Claire feel achingly sad for what she had lost. Every time they went out, they held hands. She saw them from the kitchen window walking along the shore hand in hand with Dusty trotting along ahead carrying a stick that was way too big for her.

Even Claire's little dog seemed to be

Watching them together made Claire feel achingly sad for what she had lost

"Thanks," he said despondently.

A voice inside her head told her to ask him to stay for coffee, but instead, she just stood at the open front door waiting for him to leave.

"The house looks nice," he said suddenly. "All clean and tidy."

happier in their contented presence.

They finished each other's sentences and talked non-stop. It was obvious that Helen's ploy had worked.

By the end of the weekend they were talking excitedly about getting married **Continued overleaf…**

Continued from previous page

again and returning here to the B&B for their honeymoon.

Except it wasn't really a B&B, was it? But why shouldn't it be? The idea struck Claire out of the blue. It would generate an income and might even mean she could hang on to the house. And she'd enjoyed having people to stay.

"Goodbye, dear," Joyce said, giving Claire an affectionate, massive hug. "We've had such a wonderful time. This house is every bit as warm, comfortable and welcoming as we remembered it to be. I just wish we'd come back years ago."

chest and could hear the steady thud of his heart through his sweater.

"Who were those people?" he asked. "Did they come to view the house?"

"No," she sobbed, but didn't – couldn't – say anything else.

"I had a job interview," he said tentatively. "More money, but longer hours and working away. Perhaps if we weren't so worried about money… perhaps we could…"

Claire suddenly laughed and rubbed at her tears. So he was looking for solutions too. They couldn't turn back time, but they could start over again.

She could feel his hesitation, his fear, as he tentatively put his arms around her

Trevor squeezed her hand fondly.

"Let's not agonise over the things we should have done. We're together again now, that's all that matters."

When Claire closed the door behind them, she couldn't stop the tears pouring down her face. She was crying so hard that she didn't hear the tap at the door and didn't realise anyone was there until Dusty started barking and jumping around like mad.

Quickly she wiped her tears away and opened the door.

"Did you forget something?" she began, but it wasn't Joyce and Trevor – they had gone – and it was Tony standing on the doorstep.

"Have you been crying?" he asked and his voice was so tender that she burst into tears all over again.

She could feel his hesitation, his fear, as he put his arms around her. She leaned her head against his strong, solid

"You don't have to change your job," she said, taking a deep breath. "Come in, Tony. I'll make coffee and tell you all about my plans."

"Plans?" he looked worried.

"Plans for our future," she said. "Our future together, in this house… if you want us to be."

Dusty ran ahead of them barking and wagging her tail. Claire didn't know if they'd live happily ever after, but there was only one way to find out.

And, as Tony held tight to her hand, she knew he'd be with her all the way.

A WORD FROM THE AUTHOR

"I think we all have those special places, either in our mind or for real, where we've been happy – and revisiting them really can work wonders."

Teatime Treat

Whoopie Pies

MAKE A TASTY BITE!

A sweet treat!

Ingredients

For the pies:
- 125g (4oz) butter or margarine, softened
- 200g (7oz) caster sugar
- 1 large egg, beaten
- 1tsp vanilla extract
- 400g (14oz) self raising flour
- 150ml (¼pt) whole milk

For the topping:
- 175g (6oz) icing sugar
- Sugar strands and hundreds and thousands to decorate

For the filling:
- 150g (5oz) unsalted butter, softened
- 250g (9oz) icing sugar
- A few drops vanilla extract

Preparation time: 30mins plus cooling and setting
Cooking time: 15mins
Makes 8

● Preheat oven to 180°C , Fan Oven 160°C, Gas Mark 4. Line 3 large baking trays with baking parchment. In a mixing bowl, cream the **butter** or margarine and **sugar** together until pale and creamy then beat in the **egg** and **vanilla extract**. Gradually sieve in **flour** and add **milk**, stirring well.
● Using a 5cm (2in) diameter ice-cream scoop, drop scoops of the mixture on to each baking tray, spaced well apart – you should be able to make 16. Bake in the oven for about 15mins until risen, lightly golden and firm to the touch. Cool for 10mins before transferring to a wire rack.
● For the topping, mix the **icing sugar** with 5-6tsp warm water and spread over the peaked side of half the cold pies. Sprinkle with **cake decorations**.
● To fill, beat the **butter** in a mixing bowl and sieve in the **icing sugar**. Add the **vanilla extract** and spread thickly over the flat sides of the remaining pie halves. Sandwich 2 halves together.

RECIPES: KATHRYN HAWKINS PHOTOGRAPHY: LIGHTHOUSE PHOTOGRAPHY

White Horses

It was the last thing he thought he wanted, being whisked off on a voyage of rediscovery, but a wife often knows best

By Jan Wright

D oug spent ages wandering around the bleak, empty shop, which oddly looked much smaller now it was devoid of stock. It was hard to leave, but he'd taken the final meter readings four times now so there wasn't anything left to do except cry, and he didn't want to do that… at least, not here. So, with a twisted feeling in the pit of his stomach, he took his keys and slowly locked the front door for the very last time.

He still couldn't believe it had come to this. For thirty years he'd run his little hardware store and, whilst it hadn't made him a fortune, he'd enjoyed every minute of it. By knowing his customers he'd survived the opening of a massive

As he posted the shop keys through the landlord's door, he thought about the day he'd picked up those very same keys. Helen had encouraged him to take the risk and start his own business, and he'd been both excited and terrified. Now he was just scared of the empty days stretching out in front of him.

Perhaps he'd been stupid, but he'd always imagined he'd still be running the shop at eighty. At sixty-two, he'd never given retirement a thought. What was he going to do with the rest of his life?

Doug drove home the long way, and as he pulled onto the drive Helen came rushing towards him. He wasn't sure he could cope with tea and sympathy.

"Where have you been?" she shouted. "We've only got half an hour before we have to leave. I'll load the suitcases in

"Where have you been?" she shouted. "Get changed. We've got half an hour"

DIY superstore fifteen years ago, but he couldn't fight this recession. Nearly all his customers were affected, and a few months ago Doug realised that if he didn't close the business soon, he'd end up going bust as well.

Helen kept telling him they were lucky to be coming out with their savings intact, and he knew his wife was right. But no matter how hard he tried, Doug didn't feel lucky.

the car while you go and change." With that, she took the car keys and dashed back to the house.

He was still standing by the car looking confused when she came out lugging the first suitcase. Being a gentleman, he hurried over and took it from her. "What's going on?"

"Haven't time for explanations," Helen replied tensely, glancing at her watch. "Let's just say this is the start of

"We're off to the Isle of Wight"

our new life – and you're already running late for it."

When he didn't move, Helen gave him a quick kiss. "I promise I'll explain it all in the car, darling, but for now, please put down the case and go and get changed – quickly!"

As Doug took a fast shower, he decided tea and sympathy might have been quite nice after all.

With dripping hair, Doug climbed into the car as his wife revved the engine and shot out of the drive. Unlike him, Helen did everything in top gear, she always had done; it was one of the things Doug loved about her.

"As long as we don't hit heavy traffic we should make the ferry," Helen stated.

Doug assumed she'd planned all this to stop him coming home from the shop and falling to pieces. However, this was the end of an era and he felt he could easily fall to pieces wherever he was.

As they turned onto the motorway, Doug finally gave in and asked her where they were going.

"Guess."

Doug wasn't in the mood for guessing games and when he didn't answer, Helen gave him a clue. "I thought we'd go back to where it all began forty years ago."

"The Isle of Wight?"

She grinned. "Spot on, and you'll never guess where we're staying."

He hoped it wasn't a costly hotel.

Continued overleaf...

"It's where you used to live on Gurnard Marsh," she replied proudly.

Good grief, had she gone mad? He used to live in a tatty old railway carriage on stilts. Why on earth would she want to go back to that?

Doug couldn't believe his luck when, at twenty-one, he'd landed a job teaching sailing to youngsters. Since the age of eight he'd loved being on the water, and coming to live in Cowes and sailing every day was a dream come true. Finding affordable accommodation wasn't so easy, which was how he'd ended up living in the old railway carriage on the Marsh. He'd queried the years ago. You don't really think that railway carriage is still there? I've booked us into a chalet."

Ah, they had lots of chalets on the Marsh – most of them in a worse condition than the carriage.

"I can assure you the chalet has a fully functioning indoor bathroom," she said.

That's as maybe, Doug thought, but he bet it was still noisy when it rained, and judging by those clouds it was about to do just that. He sank lower in his car seat and wished he were home, where he could sneak off to his shed and mope in peace. He felt empty and old; revisiting his youth was the last thing he needed.

Gurnard Marsh was still little more than a row of quaint chalets beside the sea

high stilts it balanced on before agreeing to rent, and was told they stopped the carriage flooding in the exceptionally high tides twice a year. What the landlord failed to mention was that for two days every fortnight, when it was simply the normal high tides, the garden flooded. And this was a relevant point, given that the toilet was at the bottom of that garden.

His grandparents still had an outside toilet, so it hadn't worried him. At least, not until he'd stepped bleary-eyed out of his carriage a week after moving in and found himself knee-high in water. It was just the first of many paddles to the end of the garden!

The railway carriage did have its good points, but they didn't include running hot water. And when it rained it sounded like a sledgehammer hitting the roof.

When he mentioned this to Helen, she simply laughed. "Doug, that was forty

A s he sat and watched the miles go by, Doug remembered the day he met Helen. It was August, 1969, and the sailing conditions were perfect. He preferred working with the kiddies as he had no problem laughing and joking with them, whereas nineteen-year-old girls tended to make him blush a lot.

However, Helen was different. She was staying with friends in Cowes for the summer, and he immediately felt at ease with her. She'd fearlessly jumped into the little dinghy, even though she knew nothing. She'd laughed when she capsized the boat and was thrown head first into the Solent. She was hopeless at sailing, but that didn't dim her enjoyment of the whole experience.

She completely captivated him and, despite his shyness, he managed to ask her to join him on a walk one evening. After that, they spent every free moment together. By the end of her holiday, they were in love. Doug asked her to join him on the Island, but he understood when she said she'd rather live closer to her family. He left his job, moved to the Midlands and they married ten months later. He'd never once regretted it.

"The car ferry's better these days," Helen commented an hour later, as they drank coffee on the top deck.

"Most of the boats look better," Doug replied, as he studied the yachts on the Solent. It was years since he'd been sailing. He'd taken the children when they were young, but since he'd started the business he hadn't the time.

Doug drove the car off the ferry, and hoped he'd be able to remember his way around after all these years.

Finding the East Cowes floating bridge was easy. "I see some things never change," he commented, as the clunking old chains pulled them across the River Medina.

Apart from the new blocks of flats, the seafront looked exactly as Doug remembered. And Gurnard Marsh hadn't changed that much either. It

was still little more than a row of quaint chalets running parallel to the sea.

"That chalet hasn't changed a bit since my day," Doug said, pointing to a rather dilapidated building.

"But the rest have been upgraded," Helen said positively. "And that restaurant is new."

As Doug parked outside their chalet, he had to admit this one did look nice. Helen was out of the car in a flash, and rushed to open the door. Sure enough, inside it had a lovely bathroom complete with running hot water.

After they'd unpacked, Helen opened a bottle of wine. "Here's to our future," she said, as they stood on the patio.

"I'd forgotten how spectacular the sunsets are from here," Doug said, as they gazed at the blazing red sky. Maybe **Continued overleaf…**

However he tried, he couldn't feel lucky

this was helping, he thought – which reminded him that he'd just lost his business, and he found his eyes filling with tears.

Despite everything, Doug slept well that first night and Helen had to wake him the next morning. "Come on, sleepyhead!" She laughed. "It's a sunny day, and I thought we could explore."

"I'd like to take a look at Gurnard Sailing Club," Doug replied, as he dragged himself out of bed.

"All I remember are those rickety old steps up to the club house," Helen said. "I should think the place has fallen into the sea by now."

Walking to the sailing club was something Doug had done many times when he lived here. Teaching sailing in Cowes was his job, but racing his little dinghy from Gurnard was pure pleasure, and that was how he'd spent all his free time. Shame that his days on the water were all in the past.

Most of the houses looked familiar on the walk, but the sailing club had changed completely. Where once an old wooden shack had stood, there was a bright white modern building, and the Water's Edge café next door had changed as well. Just a few paces from

with sailors preparing for the morning race. As Doug walked between the boats, he was amazed to see a face he knew. The two men stared at each other; forty years had passed since they last sailed together.

"Tim, I don't believe it," Doug cried, staring at a guy in a wetsuit. "Don't tell me you're still sailing dinghies."

Actually, as Doug soon discovered, there were quite a few baby boomers in amongst the teenagers. Their hair, or what was left of it, might be grey, and there might be a few wrinkles he hadn't seen before, but he had no problem recognising them.

As he started to say hello, it felt like he'd only been away a few months. "I'm short of a crew today," one of the guys called out. "How do you fancy coming out on the boat with me?"

Doug turned to look at Helen. "Off you go," she said, giving him a little push. "I'll be happy sitting here drinking coffee and watching you."

"Are you sure?" he asked, half wishing she'd said not to be so silly and that at his age he needed to take it easy.

Less than an hour later, the race started. "You weren't hoping to win this, were you?" Doug asked, as he

There were several faces he knew. It was as if he'd only been away a few months

the beach, it was now much bigger and looked so welcoming.

"I think we'll have a coffee and cake in there later," he said, but first he wanted to see what kind of dinghies the folks around here were sailing these days.

Being a Sunday, the place was buzzing

helped haul the boat upright again. "I don't think I'm as agile as I used to be."

Luckily, by the end of the race, it had all come back to him. He didn't disgrace himself by making them come last.

"That was amazing," Doug called

Continued overleaf…

By the end of the race, it had all come back to him – and they weren't last

His muscles ached, but it was so good to be back

Continued from previous page

happily, as he strolled back to Helen.

"At first, I thought you were going to spend all your time with the boat upside down." She laughed. "But I see you managed to improve."

They stayed and had lunch at the club. Doug still couldn't get over how many people he knew here, but then why would anyone want to move away from such a beautiful location? He'd only left because he'd fallen in love with Helen.

He glanced over to see how she was, and saw she was happily chatting to a group of women.

"Do you want to crew for me again on

wasn't too old to go dinghy sailing.

"I had a feeling this would do you good," Helen said approvingly. Then they started to speak together.

"Helen, do you think we could afford to come over more often?"

"Look Doug, the family are all grown and have moved away. We could easily sell up and move over here."

"Did I hear you right?" Doug asked. "You said you'd be happy to live here?"

"It's not only the chalets that have changed over the last forty years. This would be perfect for us."

Doug threw his arms around his wife.

"The family are all grown up. We could easily sell up and move over here"

Wednesday evening?" he was asked.

"I'd love to," he replied. He didn't refuse an invitation to try out a catamaran on Tuesday afternoon either. Although, as his muscles started to remind him that he hadn't used them for a while, he did wonder if this was entirely sensible.

By the end of their week, Doug had been sailing four times and every one of his muscles ached. But instead of lying awake at night worrying, as he had recently, he'd slept soundly.

"It's been a wonderful holiday," Doug said, as they packed the car. During the week, they'd driven around the Island and they'd been delighted to see it was still as pretty as ever. Their chalet had been cosy, and the area was much nicer thanks to the pumping station that now stopped the constant flooding. But the real highlight had been realising he

"Perhaps we ought to let an estate agent look at the house next week."

"That's a great idea, I can ring…"

Helen was in full swing as her fast-action brain started planning all the things they would need to do as soon as they reached home.

Doug smiled as he started driving. Why had he been so worried about losing the business? With a wife like Helen at his side, he should have known that this wouldn't be the end of an era – simply the start of a new one.

A WORD FROM THE AUTHOR

"The inspiration for this story comes from our experience of having had to close our business recently. My baby boomer husband went straight out and bought himself a new dinghy!"

Fancy That!

Seventies

Sensational 70s facts to make you go "Wow!"

Waterloo winners

Fact!
Abba first came to fame when they won the Eurovision song contest with Waterloo in 1974

Mexican Beetle

Production shifts

The original VW Beetle ceased production in Germany in 1978, but continued to be made in Mexico until 2003

● The video game Space Invaders was created by Toshihiro Nishikado in 1978.

WOW! ● **Byran Allen pedalled the first human-powered propeller plane, the Gossamer Albatross, into flight on August 23, 1977.**

● The first flushing toilets for dogs opened in Paris in 1978.

● **The guillotine was last used in France in 1977.**

● The first "pocket" calculator, the Canon Pocketronic, out in 1970, weighed 31oz.

● **Richard Nixon was the first American president to resign, in 1974.**

WOW! ● **Solar Craft I, the world's first solar powered boat, was built by A T Freeman in 1975.**

● Among the snacks launched in the 70s were Wotsits (1970), Hula Hoops (1971), Ringos (1973), Skips (1974), Frazzles (1975), Discos (1976), Smith's Square Crisps (1976) and the crazy Monster Munch (1978).

For The Record!

German swimmer Mark Spitz won a record seven gold medals at the 1972 Olympics, and also set a new world record in each of the seven events he competed in

Raising the bar

Flip Flop Heart

The excitement of a funfair is irresistible to teenage girls, and one of this trio of friends wins more than a goldfish!

By Karen Byrom

T he smell of candyfloss and toffee apples caught in Gemma's throat as soon as she entered the fairgound with her two friends. Pop tunes floated in the air, almost but not quite, drowned out by the sound of thrilled screams as waltzers waltzed, dodgems dodged and chair-o-planes carried their excited cargo to the edge of the sky.

Gemma and Jaclyn were helping Allison to celebrate her birthday. She was thirteen and it was the first time the three friends had been allowed to come to the fair unaccompanied by their parents.

Pound coins jingled as Gemma thrust her hands into her pockets, trying to

outgoing and sassy, both girls had taken her under their wing when they'd arrived together at Preston High from different feeder primaries. Now the threesome were inseparable, but Gemma remained shy and timid while the other two blossomed – in all ways! – and began to discover boys.

"Come on!" Allison caught Gemma's hand and pulled her towards a terrifying-looking construction that proclaimed itself as Vertigo. She eyed its pods nervously – they looked small but she guessed they'd be speedy! "We'll sit on either side of you and keep you safe."

"I thought we were starting with…" Jaclyn objected. Her voice trailed off as she caught sight of a group of boys in the queue just ahead of them. Among them

Gemma prayed for the ride to stop. Had just three minutes ever lasted so long?

contain the shivers of excitement that were running through her body. It wouldn't do to look uncool – not when half the school was here on the fair's opening night.

"Where first?" Jaclyn tugged at Allison's arm. "Big wheel?"

"Waltzers!" Allison shouted.

"Teacups?" Gemma suggested.

Gemma joined in as Allison and Jaclyn dissolved into giggles at her suggestion. She knew they weren't being unkind –

was James Cargill, the fittest boy in Year Nine – and the one everyone wanted to go out with!

"Hey, James! Over here!" Allison shouted out cheekily.

Gemma's face burned as James and his friends turned round and quickly turned away again. Year Eight girls were obviously beneath their notice.

The queue dwindled proportionately to the increase in Gemma's heart-rate as they approached the terrifying-looking

The goldfish was her get-out

ride. James and three of his friends piled into the first capsule and one boy was left behind. He look annoyed.

"You can come in with us, Peter." Jaclyn grinned. "Save you hanging around 'til that lot come off."

Peter shrugged and entered the second pod. Taking his silence as acceptance, Jaclyn and Allison clambered in after him. Gemma, lodged firmly between her friends, had no choice but to get in, too.

The ride began to spin, slowly, and then with increasing velocity. Allison and Jaclyn squealed in delight and vied with each other to be thrown into Peter's lap. Peter himself maintained a stoic silence – it was obviously beneath his dignity to scream like a girl. Gemma closed her eyes and prayed she wouldn't throw up!

Had three minutes ever lasted so long? By the time the ride slowed to a stop, Gemma hoped she didn't look as green as she felt. She stumbled out of the pod **Continued overleaf…**

Continued from previous page

after Allison and Jaclyn, head
spinning – straight into the arms of
James Cargill, who had already
hopped off his own pod and was
waiting for Peter to join him.

"Get off!" he exclaimed rudely,
pushing her away.

This time she did fall, down on to
her knees. The boys laughed
uproariously and moved away in a
tight circle towards the ferris
wheel where Allison and
Jaclyn had already headed,
oblivious to her plight.

"Pigs!" Gemma shouted
after them. All she got was a
gesture in reply.

Gemma lay where she was.
Maybe if she stayed there long
enough, the ground would
swallow her up.

Suddenly she felt the grip of a strong
hand in hers, that pulled her gently, but
firmly to her feet.

"Are you okay?" Peter was still there,
his brown eyes concerned as he looked
down at her.

"I… I'm…" How was she really? She
looked around but there was no sign of
her friends. Had they seen what
happened, were they laughing with the
boys? She felt her eyes fill with tears.
Suddenly, the noise of the rides and the
press of the crowd overwhelmed her. She
wanted her mum!

"I'm okay," she said shakily.

Peter looked at her dubiously. "You
don't look okay. You shouldn't have gone
on that ride."

"I know," Gemma groaned. What a
wimp he must think she was."I hate
heights. I like rides like the carousel,
and… and the teacups!"

"I'm not going on any teacups!" Peter

Would they
last as long as
Flipper had?

grinned. "But I'll hang around 'til your
pals come back."

"Thanks," Gemma said. She looked
down at her toes, unable to think of
anything else to say. Peter, equally ill-at-
ease, looked round wildly.

"Come on!" he said suddenly. "I'll win
you a goldfish!"

Unselfconsciously, he caught her hand
and pulled her towards the nearby
shooting stall, whose proprietor was
loudly promising a goldfish to anyone
who could hit the bullseye.

"But I don't want a –"

Before she could finish her sentence,
Peter had handed over two pound coins
and received five darts in return.

He threw the first. It missed the board
completely, lodging in the wall behind.
For the second time that night, Gemma
closed her eyes. She couldn't bear to
look. Then suddenly she was aware of
the sound of cheering as a cold, wet
plastic bundle was thrust into her hand.

"There you go!" Peter grinned. "And there's your pals." With a quick ruffle of her hair, he bounded off just as Allison and Jaclyn came running up to Gemma, their faces glowing.

"There you are!" Allison exclaimed. "We thought you were right behind us at the wheel. Then when we got off we couldn't find you…"

"We sat beside James Cargill!" Jaclyn exclaimed. "His knee was nearly touching mine." She was visibly trembling with excitement.

"What have you got there?" Allison had noticed the bundle in Gemma's hand.

they carried the two goldfish he'd picked up from the petshop into the bathroom and placed them, still in their bag, into the large fishbowl.

"They'll be the same temperature by morning," Peter said. "I'll release them into the bowl before the girls get up."

"What a birthday surprise." Gemma laughed. "Do you think they'll last as long as Flipper did?"

"I don't know." Peter looked solemn. "But it shouldn't be too hard to beat a record of forty minutes!"

He'd found her crying beside the

Peter had helped her and held her hand and won her a flippy, floppy goldfish

Gemma looked down at the goldfish in its plastic pouch then lifted a hand to her hair, where Peter had touched it.

So what if he'd treated her like a little sister? He'd helped her up and held her hand and won her a goldfish – that was way better than nearly touching stupid James Cargill's knee.

And then she realised that he'd given her the perfect get-out…

"It's a goldfish." She grinned. "A flippy, floppy goldfish." She gazed at her chums. "So I won't be able to come on any more rides with you – I might spill Flipper's water and then he wouldn't survive. But I'll watch you both from the sides."

Have you got the bowl ready?" Peter asked excitedly.

"It's in the bathroom," Gemma replied. "I filled it with water this morning and stuck it in the cupboard under the sink so the twins wouldn't notice."

Giggling like two thirteen-year-olds,

helter-skelter, Flipper floating forlornly upside down in his plastic bag, and had marched back with her to the sideshow to demand another fish!

Flipper II was more fortunate. By the time Peter and Gemma began dating, three years later, he had a companion called Skippy – and had lived to see the couple he helped bring together wed and have a family.

Tomorrow, to celebrate the twins' fifth birthday, they were all going to the funfair. And this time Gemma had the perfect excuse to stick to the kiddy rides!

A WORD FROM THE AUTHOR

"My inspiration for this story came from my fear of heights! My nephew persuaded me to go with him on a funfair ride and I came off feeling green! Sadly, there was no handsome young man waiting to win me a goldfish."

Counting Your Blessings

With a loving wife, and his old pals to look out for him, Trevor realised that life didn't get any better than this…

By Louise Stevens

D id I fall asleep just then? I must have done, but I don't know for how long. The sky out there is ink-black still.

Yes, I remember now – I was thinking about love and romance. It was something Hiker said earlier that set me off. Anyway, there isn't much else I can do, but sit and ponder the mysteries of life. At least it's dry in here and the water hasn't risen any higher. That's a blessing.

"Always count your blessings, Trevor," my mother used to say. How right she

smock dress, with ribbons in her hair. The other children heeded her immediately, of course, because little Adeline always knew her own mind.

"One day, Trevor," she told me, when we were about six or seven, "We shall be married and I shall have one boy baby and one girl baby, and we'll all live together in a nice little house."

I did not shine at school. For me, holidays were the best part, setting off with my pals, Gerry and Jim, to swim in the deep, murky waters of Quarry Pool. The stream that fed it was clear, though, and teeming with sticklebacks, ripe for

I did not shine at school. The holidays were the best part, really good times

was. After my father's early demise, Mother found love again. He was a good man, Mr Spoon, and a fine stepfather to me. But I'll never forget my first morning at school. There'd been some giggles when my name was called from the register, and as I stepped out into the schoolyard the chants began –

"Teaspoon, teaspoon."

"Be quiet!" someone yelled at them, and there stood Adeline Brown, in a

catching in a jar. Those were good times.

Jim persuaded us to go apple-scrumping once, in Hiker Tulledge's orchard. I told him no good would come of it and I was proved right. Hiker didn't catch us, but we had our comeuppance. I've never touched an unripe apple since.

Good times.

Then, one by one, my pals started walking out, first with one girl, then another. Suddenly, all Jim and Gerry's

She was a girl whose words everyone heeded

talk was of love and romance, quarrels, making-up and engagements. And this is what I've been pondering over. All that excitement was happening around me and yet, thinking back, I had no part in it. Though I can't remember how it came about, I never thought of marrying anyone but Adeline.

And what man had a better home than I? When, in all these years, have I not returned to a nourishing meal, a tidy house, and our son and daughter so

respectful? In fact, if I'd gone straight home to Adeline tonight, I wouldn't be in this predicament now!

Of course, a man must provide for his family. The warehouse where I found employment was only a short bicycle ride away – not too steep – which, as Adeline pointed out, was a blessing, since we never needed a car.

"Your title is Clerk of General Duties," said the manager on my first day at the **Continued overleaf…**

Continued from previous page

warehouse, as he handed me a broom.

It's almost ten years since I left. As I relinquished the bunch of keys to my own Clerk of General Duties, I wondered whether he would stay long enough to become manager, as I did. There's much

know how long I've been here. It's getting a bit chilly now.

Adeline insisted I wore my mackintosh tonight, though it's only September. She was right of course. Earlier on, as I climbed the stone steps of the Last

Even when the weather turns foul, we squeeze into Jim's hut on the allotment

to be thankful for in having a fair pension and a sound heart.

Some men are bored in retirement. Not me. Even when the weather turns foul, all of us on the allotments squeeze into Jim's hut to brew tea and talk about next season's crop. I think that, for Adeline, it's a double blessing, all that fresh food and not having me under her feet all the time.

Talking about time – I wish I'd remembered to put my watch on, then I'd

Unicorn, a great gust of wind almost swung the sign off its hinges.

"Rough night, Mr Spoon," our landlord remarked. "The usual?"

I've been buying a beer from Gordon, and his father before him, most Friday nights for decades. Adeline has views on strong liquor, but one pint is quite mellowing, I find. When I took my place at our usual table, the others were already there – Jim, Gerry and Hiker.

There was a power cut and the phones were down...

"Ev'nin, Teaspoon," Jim and Gerry chorused, and old Hiker nodded a friendly greeting.

Now there's another mystery – Hiker's age. No one in the village seems to know it. He's still spry and there's nothing he enjoys more than a game of dominoes, except maybe a malt whisky. His cottage is only fifty yards from the Last Unicorn, and someone always sees him safely home. This evening, I was the one to take him; the two of us huddled against walls while the gale did its best to blow us over.

"Come in out of the wind," he shouted, when we reached his front door.

Once inside, I noticed Hiker's mantel clock said half past ten.

"D'ye know what today is, Trevor?" Hiker asked me.

"Friday," I replied.

"Nay," he said. "'Tis my birthday."

"Happy Birthday, Hiker!" I wished him.

He began filling a battered kettle. "I'll put the water on for a quick brew," he said.

Adeline expects me by a quarter to eleven but, not to disappoint my old friend, I waited while Hiker busied himself in the little alcove that serves as his kitchen.

"You seem to manage very well by yourself here, Hiker," I remarked.

"But were you never in love, Hiker?" I persisted, looking at my friend.

"Countless times," he said. "I've known many a wild romance in my day. But," he turned to me with a wicked grin on his face, "I never let one of 'em catch me."

He handed me a cup of tea.

"There," he said, "this'll warm thee."

Taking his own cup, he settled into his old leather armchair. The wind could be heard howling even inside the thick cottage walls. I peered through Hiker's front window for a minute, then turned back to face his chair, saying, "Here's to you, Hiker, many happy returns."

I drained the cup – it was strong and bitter, but anything warm was welcome on such a night. There was only the sound of deep snoring.

Watching him, I couldn't help making comparisons between the two of us – this one-time Lothario, living out his days in happy solitude – and me, a man who has never in his life known what it is to go back to an empty house.

Rather than disturb him, I eased Hiker's cup from his grasp and to save waste, drank it down as well. Taking a blanket from the other chair, I wrapped it snugly round him, checked the stove was

"I've know many a wild romance in my day, but I've never let 'em catch me"

"Aye," he said proudly. "I'm used to fendin' for myself, Trevor."

For as long as I've known Hiker, he's always lived alone. There was a matter I've always been curious about.

"Didn't you ever think of marrying?" I asked him now.

"Me? Nay," he replied, his thin shoulders shaking with laughter.

safe, and left Hiker to dream the night away.

His door latch clicked into place behind me. Seconds later, the yellow pool of light from the street lamp popped out, leaving only glimmers of a thin moon between scudding clouds. I couldn't even make out the windows of the Last Unicorn, and the red sign that usually **Continued overleaf…**

Continued from previous page

flickers "Post Office" had disappeared altogether. I could have turned back to Hiker's cottage, but home was seven minutes walk away; to the end of the road and left along the lane. Adeline would be waiting, sitting in her blue dressing gown and slippers, listening for my key in the lock. "Was it a good evening?" she would have asked. And I would have replied, "Yes," and followed her upstairs.

So I picked my way forwards to the corner where the lane begins and the pavement changes to uneven gravel. But the route I know well had become a winding path that seemed to move beneath my feet. I forged on and on, the wind roaring above and around me, my head so low that I very nearly ran into a large wooden post.

"Thank goodness!" I said to myself, looking up. "I know where I am."

Catching my breath, I held on to the sign marked "Allotment Holders Only". Rather than risk getting lost again, I decided to make for Jim's hut and shelter until the wind died down.

And here's another mystery! There'd

was nothing I could do but sit there and wait out the storm.

And here I've been ever since. At least Adeline is safe at home. And Jim's rocking chair is comfortable…

I think I fell asleep again. The wind has stopped altogether now, but still the sky is black as pitch. It must be well past midnight by now. Whatever will Adeline be thinking?

Wait! Was I dreaming, or did someone call my name? There it is again. And there are lights – five or six of them, dancing across the horizon. Now I can hear many people all talking at once.

"Be quiet!" one of them calls out loudly. "Just listen!"

It's that voice – a woman's – that has me scuffling from my hiding place.

"Adeline?" I call back. "Is that you?"

The lights join together. The voices are getting nearer now.

"Trevor? Where are you?"

"Mr Spoon?"

"Teaspoon?"

"There he is, just over there, look!"

"We've looked for you everywhere, Trevor," Adeline says, dabbing her eyes

been no rain, yet water was streaming past on either side as I trudged up the cobbled way through the allotments. I could see the outline of a building. I made towards it, stumbled up the steps and shut the door behind me.

When I peered out of the window, water was still bubbling past. Even if someone had left the standpipe running, I reasoned, it would have been no more than a trickle.

There's been a deluge, I decided. There

I recognise Jim's son, our constable. Jim is here too, and Gerry and his son Gordon, all rushing and stumbling towards my sanctuary.

"Wait there, Mr Spoon," instructs Gordon, "while I get something for you to walk on. It's lucky you managed to find shelter. A tree was blown down and blocked the stream near Quarry Pool. The lower allotments are flooded. It's at least three inches deep."

And here is Adeline, wearing my

Hiker made a nightcap

these good friends come to my aid!

Several hands reach out to help me across the plank as, thankfully, I step off into Adeline's waiting arms.

"I'm so grateful to you all, for finding him," Adeline tells them. "Though I'll never understand how he got so lost. The allotments are in the opposite direction!"

"It's a mystery all right, Mrs Spoon," say Jim. "But a man could take a wrong turn in the dark. Anyway, let's get you both home. You and Teaspoon must be in need of a good sleep."

Adeline doesn't seem to notice the nickname. We're looking at each other, knowing, without words, that all's well. Just the way it's always been.

I see it now. It's been a little short on excitement, perhaps, but I wouldn't exchange our years of marital harmony for all the wild romance in the world.

Jim is right. This has been a strange night and I'm truly tired, even though somehow, I've managed to sleep right through a gale! When we get home, I'll tell Adeline everything that's happened.

"We'd have been here much sooner," Gordon is saying as we all walk off, "but it took a long time to wake old Hiker. I blame the double whisky he pours in his tea as a nightcap."

Perhaps, on reflection, I'll just go home and sleep. There's one small but important point about marital harmony – knowing when to count your blessings and keep silent.

rubber gardening boots and a coat over her dressing gown. But something is very wrong, because she has tears running down her cheeks.

"What is it?" I ask.

"We've looked for you everywhere, Trevor," she says, swiftly dabbing her eyes. "When you didn't come home, I waited until nearly midnight, thinking you were stuck at the Last Unicorn, because of the power cut."

"A power cut?" I repeat, trying to take all these details in.

"The phone lines are down," Jim adds. "Mrs Spoon knocked on our door. She was in such a state. We went to look for you at the Unicorn."

Adeline? In a state?

"What time is it?"

"About four in the morning," says Gordon, wading over with a plank, which he sets across the mud. "We tried Hiker's cottage, thinking you might have taken shelter with him."

I'm heartily wishing I had done. But what a blessing – that I should have all

A WORD FROM THE AUTHOR

"Looking at an old school photograph recently, I realised that at least one marriage was eventually formed from the group."

ILLUSTRATIONS: MASTERFILE, MANDY MURRAY

The Love List

Will indecisive Emily catch the eye of gorgeous Ben, or settle for easy-going Tony? Enjoy this light-hearted tale

By Jill Steeples

mily sat at her desk, gazing out of the window, lost in thought, a pen held to her lips. She was making a list. It was something she'd learned from her mother.

"If you don't know what to do, write it down: the pros and cons." At the time, she was talking about Emily's indecision over her options at school, whether to study another language or one of the sciences. "Seeing it in black and white can help make up your mind."

Her mum had been right; she chose German and didn't regret it once.

That was a long time ago, but Emily would still resort to pen and paper when weighing up her options – when deciding whether to join the travel agents where she worked, and when she bought her car.

and *sensitive* as she had those covered. She did want to make it a fair assessment.

It was proving difficult, though. Under "Cons" she'd only managed two things: *doesn't like soap operas* and *Tania Hardy.* She wondered if not liking particular TV programmes counted as a character fault, but as she was struggling to come up with anything else, she decided it could stay.

Tania Hardy was a big con, though. A close friend of Ben's, she hung around with him at the rugby club, waiting in the bar after a game. She'd also taken to turning up at the book club where Emily had met Ben, although Emily suspected she hadn't read any of the club's offerings.

"I can think of more exciting ways to spend my time," she'd told Emily, her gaze travelling to Ben's broad figure encased in loose jeans and a white T-shirt.

Sighing, Emily crumpled the paper. Ben

Whatever his charms, he just wasn't available. So she might as well have fun

This list, though, was different. She'd written, in red ink, "Ben Adamson" and underneath "Pros and Cons", heavily underlined. Around his name, Emily had drawn a heart and beside it she'd experimented with her initials, EB, entwined with his, BA. Under "Pros" she had listed: *good-looking, kind, funny, sporty, tall, slim, patient.* She swooned, before deciding she had to be more selective, scrubbing out *gorgeous, athletic*

wasn't available. And he'd hardly be interested in someone like her.

"Why don't you come out with us tonight?" Wendy, her supervisor, was standing at her desk.

"I've already tried," interrupted Tony, the sales manager. "It's her book club."

"Ah well." Wendy smiled. "Next time."

"Actually," said Emily, thinking it'd not hurt if she missed one session, "if there's a place for me, I'd love to come."

It was a foolproof method – until now!

Aztec Travel organised regular social functions for its employees, but Emily wasn't really one for group activities.

Standing in the harsh lights of the bowling alley, music throbbing, she wondered if she should have given tonight a miss. But once she lost her self-consciousness and Tony had given her a few tips on rolling the ball, she found herself enjoying the experience.

"You're a natural!" Tony said, punching the air as she scored a strike.

Afterwards, they went to the pizza restaurant next door and Emily, ravenous from her exertions, munched her way through a whole pepperoni thin crust.

Later, back in her flat, Emily thought what an unexpectedly good time she'd had. She'd gone a whole three hours without even thinking about Ben. *Yes,* she thought smiling, *a very good evening.*

The following morning the alarm and telephone joined forces to rally Emily from her bed. Wearily, she silenced the clock and clambered out of bed.

"Hello?" she said, groggily.

Continued overleaf…

Continued from previous page

"Emily, it's Ben. I just wanted to check you were okay. When you didn't turn up last night, I thought you might be poorly."

Caring, thought Emily, mentally adding to her list. *Seductive voice.*

"Oh, hi, Ben. I'm fine, thank you. I had something on at work. And to be honest," she continued, "I really struggled with that last book. Science fiction's not my thing."

Hearing the warmth in Ben's laugh, she imagined his nut-brown eyes creasing in amusement. "It left me cold, too," he said. "There's a Victorian-era whodunnit next."

"Yes, it should be more entertaining."

"Actually, there's something else." He sounded tentative. "There's a big match on Saturday, the last of the season. We're having a bit of a do afterwards at the club. I wondered if you'd like to come along."

Emily smiled. Did she already have "considerate" on her list? In fact Tania had told her all about the party, how Ben had asked her to accompany him and whether she should wear her red floaty dress.

"That's nice of you, Ben." Whatever issues Emily had with him were all of her own making. "Thanks," she said decisively. "I'd love to."

The day of the match dawned. Rain. Emily felt certain it wouldn't be of too much concern to a bunch of burly rugby players, but was glad she wouldn't be out on the pitch with them and carefully timed her arrival at the clubhouse to coincide with the celebrations moving indoors.

She knew from the noise that the team must have won. She was glad when Tania made her way through the noisy, cheerful crowd to greet her.

"Did you see the match?" she asked, wide-eyed. "Ben was a real star, scored three tries and set up the winning one. He was caked in mud! Man of the match."

Emily smiled. Tania probably had her own "Ben Adamson, Pros and Cons" list.

"Look, there's Ben now! Catch you later." Tania tottered off in her heels to where Ben was receiving a great deal of backslapping. He saw Emily and beckoned, but Tania took his arm and guided him in the other direction.

Returning his smile, Emily went in search of the bar. She'd have one drink, she decided, then make her excuses.

"Emily! I didn't have you down as a rugby fan." She was delighted to see Tony.

"I'm just a friend of one of the players. I've popped in to offer my congratulations and then I'll be off home."

"So soon? I was hoping you'd be staying for the raucous singing and dancing."

Emily giggled. "I don't think so."

With Tony at her side, Emily relaxed. He was good company and made her forget herself. Unlike Ben, whose mere presence had a most disconcerting effect. When he appeared beside them, kissing her cheek, the whole room could see her blush.

"Emily. So pleased you could make it."

"Congratulations!" she said, her skin tingling. "I hear you had a great game." Ben chuckled modestly. Their eyes locked.

"Oh, do you know Tony?" she stuttered.

"Very pleased to meet you," Ben said. Emily added *polite* to her list.

Soon the two men were discussing the game, Emily nodding at what she thought were pertinent moments. When Tania joined them, entrancing Tony and Ben with her knowledge of rugby, Emily felt even more out of her depth. Smiling wryly she wondered if they were compiling their own list, "Tania Hardy, Pros and Cons". She couldn't imagine there'd be any cons.

As Tania and Tony discussed the merits of team formations, Ben moved to Emily's side. "Listen, Emily, I wondered –" Before

"I wanted to apologise," he said. "I invited you, then barely spoke to you."

"Don't be silly. I could see you were in demand. I was glad to share your big day."

"I have to admit it's a bit of a haze now, but I remember chatting to you and, um, Tony and thinking how lovely you looked."

Did he really just say she looked lovely?

"Tell me to mind my own business, but is Tony your boyfriend?"

A ray of hope sprang in Emily's chest. "Oh no, he's just a friend. I work with him."

"That's good," said Ben. "Tania couldn't stop talking about him."

Emily tried to quell her disappointment. "But, you and Tania… I thought…"

Ben laughed. "Good grief, no. I'm glad she's turned her attentions to Tony. Tania's

Hearing his voice, Emily couldn't feel anything but ridiculously pleased

he could finish, he was hijacked by his team mates and hoisted into the air.

"Ah," said Tony, "it looks as though the real partying starts here." He glanced at Tania. "She seems like a great girl."

"Yes, great fun," agreed Emily. "But I think I'll escape, if you don't mind."

"Me too." Tony looked wistfully at Tania. "I've an early start. I'll see you to your car."

Emily just managed to catch Ben's eye and wave as Tony escorted her out.

Back home, she felt relief knowing she wouldn't see Ben for three weeks. Time, she hoped, to get her emotions in check.

B ut, of course, that depended on Ben keeping his distance. How was he to know she'd set up a no-contact zone? When, next day, his gorgeous tones on the phone set her insides melting, she couldn't feel anything but ridiculously pleased.

a great girl, but she can be a bit full-on."

Ah, good judge of character, thought Emily, relieved. That list of hers would be running to two pages very soon.

"I wondered," she said, with a surge of boldness, "if you'd like to meet for a drink? We could chat about that new book."

"Hey," said Ben, his voice singing. "I was about to ask you the same thing."

Shy with women. Definitely a bonus!

"Well," she said, "in that case, I'd love to."

After all, *not liking soap operas* alone was hardly reason to refuse.

A WORD FROM THE AUTHOR

"I'm a great list-maker. It brings order to my chaotic mind; ticking off items, however small, feels like I've achieved something."

Into The Light

Jess was proud of her independence – until she learned that even the best caver needs a helping hand

By A Millward

Jess, we know there's something you're not telling us."

I freeze midway through hauling myself out of a tunnel. If I wasn't horizontal, my stomach would have dropped. The beams of three headlamps pan my way, blinding. "What are you talking about, Danny?"

"We've been down here four days and you've had 'secret' written all over you from the start," Aaron chips in, ever Danny's puppet. How did they know?

"We're going to find out eventually, Jess," Danny continues.

Finding my feet, I throw a reel of rope in the direction of Danny's voice. "You're not going to find out eventually, because there's nothing to find out!"

"What do you think, guys? There's always the tried and tested method," his teeth flash wickedly as he playfully flexes the rope. "I wonder if our baby sister's

"Don't worry. No one's coming anywhere near my feet – not unless they want me to reveal who they really kissed at the College Masquerade Ball."

By the look on his face, it's time for Danny's stomach to dive.

"I figured not," I say, patting some of the cave dust from my yellow all-in-one suit triumphantly. That was close – too close. I need to keep a tighter rein on my feelings. "So are we going to stand here waffling like Auntie Beatrice all day, or are we going to cave?"

For most people, this would be a place of nightmares. But not for me. To me, this subterranean world of labyrinths and shadows has always been a sanctuary. Down here, I can forget all about the things I spend my life worrying about on the surface. Paying the gas bill. Traffic jams. Family domestics and neighbours from hell. All I have to concentrate on here is squeezing through slimy burrows, making sure crampons are fixed soundly

I'm beginning to realise there are some problems that just can't be left behind

feet are as ticklish as they used to be?"

"Give her a break," Leo says, stepping between me and my interrogators. At 30, Leo's only a year my senior and has always done his best to protect me from my eldest brother's jibing.

I rest my hands on Leo's shoulders.

into the rock and generally not plunging into the abyss. Except I'm beginning to realise there are some problems that simply can't be left behind…

I knew it was bad news as soon as the assistant called my name in the waiting

The cave labyrinths were my sanctuary

room. She was smiling, but I saw it in her eyes; the well-rehearsed apology waiting in the wings. There was the same awkwardness in the doctor's eyes. What a horrible job they had. It was crazy because, there I was about to be told that the tiny lump I'd found in my breast was a ticking time-bomb, as I'd feared all along, yet I was feeling sorry for them.

"What are my options, Doctor?" I was straight down to business.

"Perhaps I should tell you a little more about the findings first," he suggested.

"If it's all the same with you, Doctor, I can do without knowing the ins. All I'm interested in hearing about are the outs."

He tried to persuade me to hear more about the tumour, the benefits of group counselling and whether or not I wanted them to contact anyone. But my ears were closed to all but the cure.

"We'll start the chemotherapy next week," he eventually conceded.
Continued overleaf…

For all my pressing for an answer, I was suddenly thrown by how fast this was happening. Perhaps it was the realisation that this couldn't be cured with pills and a little bedrest. You heard so many bad things about chemo – or was the shock more to do with the fact I'd just found out I had breast cancer at just 29 years old?

"I can't do next week," I said like a pre-recorded message playing on behalf of someone away from home. "It's the family caving trip. My brothers and I do it every year. We're going to Italy. It's been arranged since last March."

"Well, I strongly suggest you postpone it. This is very serious…"

"No!" I snapped. "Sorry, Doctor, no. It can't be postponed. March 17. It's the same every year. It was our dad's birthday. The chemotherapy will just have to wait another week."

"Mrs Lewis," he'd pleaded. "I can't stress just how important timing is in these situations."

I was getting to my feet, and the Doctor and his assistant were looking to system which affords so much headroom. I watch closely where he puts his hands, knees, elbows, feet – following the basic three-points-of-contact-at-all-times rule.

I can hear Danny and Leo up ahead, arguing over the result of a recent football match. Somewhere, far, far above us other tourists are swilling wine, examining crumbling ruins and ordering pizza. But I wouldn't swap the primordial peace down here for anything, nor the dark walls that burst with stars at the kiss of our headlamps.

"I know," I reply. "I've forgotten about it – you should too." If only time-bombs tick-ticking inside were as easy to forget.

I almost tell him. Words along the lines of *Aaron, you and Danny were right – there is something I've been keeping from everyone* are on the tip of my tongue, but my brother beats me to the moment with, "You really are cool, Jess – for a sister, I mean."

"Wow, steady on, Aaron. With compliments like that, my head will grow too big to fit through the next tight spot."

I almost tell him – the words on the tip of my tongue – but my brother speaks

one another like a pair of startled deer.

Once again I felt a flash of sympathy. Did they have to deal with as many headstrong patients as they did bad test results? "I accept full responsibility for my actions, Doctor, but this is something I have to do. Nothing you can say is going to change my mind."

Y ou know, he was only teasing earlier," Aaron says over his shoulder later, as we scramble our way through a large cavern – one of the few in this

As it turns out the next tight spot isn't that far away. We always take these squeezes in turn. This time, the role of guinea pig falls on me. After this many years caving, I can generally tell from how much I struggle to negotiate a gap whether my heftier brothers will pass or need to find an alternative route.

Pressing myself against the stone, I mould myself into the traditional Superman position; one arm stretched forward, pulling with my hands, propelling with my feet. Beginners often

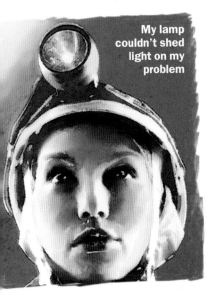

My lamp couldn't shed light on my problem

around a vertical ledge in the middle. To be honest, instinct pulled me through more than any conscious skill.

"You'll have to hold in your beer bellies," I call back, "but you'll be okay."

I hear a series of scraping and grunting as Danny enters the gap, quickly followed by a yelp, some groans and a string of expletives. Then, a defeated silence.

Dumping my gear, I dive back in. "Danny? Are you all right?"

"No, I'm bloody-well not," he grumbles. "I'm stuck."

"Stuck? Are you sure?"

"Well I haven't decided to set up camp here for the night!" he snaps, panting.

"All right, all right. Getting angry isn't going to get you out. Have you tried –?"

"I've tried everything," Danny pre-empts me. "My left arm's wedged between the rock and my kit-bag; I can't go backwards because I'm fighting gravity and it doesn't matter which way I twist, I can't work my way forward. It's like I'm caught in a U-bend."

With some difficulty, we explain what is happening to Leo and Aaron through the limited space not blocked by Danny. Once we've established that he definitely isn't going anywhere, no matter how hard they push and I pull, we eventually work out a plan. I'll wait with Danny and try to cut through his kit bag to dislodge it, while Leo and Aaron seek out an alternative route through to my end.

No one says anything, but we're all praying that their added brute strength will be enough to haul him through. Other options are running low.

Of course, there's something else that nobody's saying. I had passed through first; I should have taken more notice, I could have prevented this.

Continued overleaf…

make the mistake of trying to crawl on their knees, but this wastes valuable space. *Don't try to fight it; become part of the rock*. That's what our dad had taught us on our early caving trips.

I wish Dad was still around. Because whether it was underground or overground, he was my real Superman. He would have known exactly what I needed to hear when I found out about the cancer.

This is just another dark cave before us and we'll make it to the other side together, kid, like we always have. But imagining what he'd say is not the same as hearing him say it, huddled to his broad chest, where nothing bad could ever reach me.

Caving is all about self-reliance. Since losing Dad, the philosophy has dominated my life – at least up until last week. Right now my inner strength has crumbled. I feel like a cave-in.

"Do we have a goer?" Danny calls after me, several minutes on, after I've dripped out into the next underground room. It's a tough call. The tunnel was fairly short, but had involved a fair bit of contortion

His flickering lamp is threatening to go out altogether. "I'm just going to fetch my knife," I tell Danny. "I'll be straight back."

I begin to shuffle back, but as I do, my brother reaches out and grabs my wrist. "Please, Jess. Don't go."

He doesn't sound like the Danny I know… smaller… scared? Surely not.

"It's okay," I squeeze his hand. "I'm not going anywhere."

We settle into an awkward silence to match our awkward position. The pause must play on both our consciences, as we both begin to speak simultaneously.

Danny waves his free hand. "Ladies first," he says.

"I should have warned you better."

He shakes his head. "These things are hard to gauge. Anyway, I should have been more careful."

I smile and a few beats pass. "Your turn. What were you going to say?"

"I wanted to apologise." Danny bites his lip, clearly in two minds. Just then his helmet lamp splutters out completely, throwing his face into darkness. I go to reposition my headlamp, but he tells me to leave it, preferring oblivion. "I wanted to apologise for earlier. Everyone's entitled to their secrets. In fact, I think I've owed you an apology for a while, Jess."

"What on earth for?"

"For always tormenting you."

"I thought that's what older brothers were for," I joke.

"Don't make excuses for me, Jess. You're my little sister. I should be looking after you, especially since…" he hesitates. "But I've just carried on as always. I've let the old man down. I've let everyone down."

I wish I could hug him right now. "Danny, no one expects you to become a surrogate father, least of all me. In fact,

Caving is about self-reliance

I'd hate it if you did. Besides, some things no one can help with…"

"Jess? Jess, look at me." I can't see him in the dimness, but I feel pinned under his gaze. "What is it you're not telling me? No more games. What's wrong?"

Tick, tick, the time-bomb pounds on. "They found a tumour, in my left breast."

"What?"

"I noticed it a few weeks ago, went in for a scan. They confirmed it last week."

"But you're only twenty nine."

"It seems cancer isn't choosy, Danny. It can strike anyone, anytime. It's been caught early and the treatment stands a good chance of success."

"No wonder you've been distracted! But wait, if you're supposed to be having treatment, why the hell are you here? What does Mum say?"

Now I wish my headlamp would go out and leave my shamed face in shadow. "Mum doesn't know. No one does. As for why I'm here, I've been asking myself the same question since I got on the plane."

"And?"

I shake my head. "I think it was not wanting to let the cancer come between me and my life. Perhaps I needed to prove I wasn't scared of it," I admit.

"You've got nothing to prove when it comes to bravery, kid. You're the strongest person I know; coping with everything like you did when Dad died. Our family was stuck fast in a dark place, just like I am now, and you were the one who pulled us through, Jess."

"You're giving me too much credit."

"Don't be modest. I owe you one. More than one, in fact. As soon as we get home, you're calling your doctor and booking the first therapy session." His gloved hand reaches toward me, grazes my cheek. "We'll see this to the other side – together, okay, kid?"

I nod, not trusting myself to speak right now, because for a fleeting moment,

all his might. "I can't – if I could – just –"

The next thing I know, he's all but fallen on top of me, a tangle of limbs and equipment and ropes.

"What do you know about that," he says, "I think I'm free."

Squirming backwards until I feel open space, I carefully drop down. Danny, who's most certainly released, follows.

"I know they say laughter's the best medicine," he says, stretching, "but I never knew it was also the answer to getting unstuck."

"Hmm," I murmur, far from convinced. Something's not quite adding up…"

"What?" he asks, raising his eyebrows. "Why are you looking at me like that?"

"Danny, just how stuck were you?"

The inner strength that Dad taught me has crumbled and I feel like a cave-in

it feels like Dad's here with us and I take comfort in the fact a little of our father lives on in Danny.

"Now where do you suppose those brothers of ours have got to, without you or me there to guide them?"

I laugh. "To give them credit, they're not the ones suffering with massive denial issues or stuck in a U-bend."

I hear a sigh in the darkness. "Do you always have to be so right?"

"Hey, take it as a compliment – I've learnt from all of my brothers' mistakes."

He starts to laugh. Uncontrollable, hard-to-breathe laughter. Infectious. I'm scared we're going to start a cave-in.

"Don't – make – me – laugh," he gasps. "It hurts – in – this position."

"Stop – making – me laugh – then!" I say, turning my light in his direction.

"Seriously," Danny says, wriggling with

He smiles knowingly. "Enough for me to be a good brother – for once."

I want to be angry at his deception, but I find myself smiling back.

It seems I might not have everything right after all, because not only have I underestimated Danny, but I've also misjudged myself. Self-reliance is all well and good, but even the best caver knows when it's time to accept a helping hand from a team-mate.

Just as a sister should from her brother.

ILLUSTRATIONS: ISTOCKPHOTO, THINKSTOCK PHOTOS, MANDY MURRAY

A WORD FROM THE AUTHOR

"Last year, I went caving for the first time in Budapest; the experience was exhilirating and nerve-wracking all at once – like nothing else I've ever done."

If Mum's The Word

A simple misunderstanding? Words can create far from simple barriers that only a good friend can help you leap

By Christine Sutton

Polly's features were ghostly in the porch-light. "I'm late," she said dully.

Claire didn't hesitate. "I'll give you a lift," she offered, reaching for her coat. "Where are you going this time of night anyway? It's a quarter past ten."

Polly shook her head. "No, I'm not late to go anywhere, I'm *late*," she repeated, stressing the last word.

Claire's eyes widened. "Oh, my goodness! *That* sort of late."

She stood aside and her neighbour trailed miserably through to the kitchen.

"What do I do?" Polly cried, lifting her tiny frame onto the tallest of the breakfast bar's three chrome metal stools. It was always her favourite perch

Ah, well. Flicking the switch on the kettle she took two squat brown coffee mugs from the drainer and spooned in instant, before perching her well-padded backside on the lower of the stools.

"What do you mean, do?"

"Well, I'm late," Polly repeated earnestly. "So what happens now?"

Ever since Polly and Sam had moved in next door and found the previous owner had inadvertently left the garden hose running, turning the back garden into a miniature boating lake, Polly had been convinced that her five-years-older neighbour had the answer to all of life's little problems.

Claire's solution back then had been a line of yard brooms to sweep the flood out into the alleyway between their two houses. This, however, was something

"Correct me if I'm wrong, Pol, but you don't seem exactly ecstatic about this"

and just about the only time the five-feet-nothing nursery nurse was taller than anyone else.

A few steps behind her, Claire shot a wistful glance in at the TV, where the two-part murder mystery she'd been watching was reaching its conclusion.

way beyond her bachelor girl experience.

"Well, if you don't want to wait 'til Monday to see your doctor, I imagine you get one of those over-the-counter test kits," she suggested, adding sugar to the mugs. "How late are you, anyway?"

"Three days," Polly said glumly.

depressed tone made Claire pause. "Correct me if I'm wrong, Pol, but you don't seem exactly ecstatic about this," she said. "For what it's worth, I think you'd make a terrific mum. So what's the problem?"

"Sam," Polly answered, her sweet face pensive. "He's going to be furious. We sort of agreed to wait three years. Eight months doesn't quite cut it. We'd got it all planned, you see. Splash out on a really good holiday next year to make up for the honeymoon we couldn't afford, update the car the year after, and then save, save, save. He wanted us to get ourselves a reasonable buffer before the babies started arriving."

"Even so," Claire reasoned. "I mean, a baby. He'll come round, surely? It's great if you can have all that other stuff, but when push comes to shove it doesn't really matter, does it?"

Polly grimaced. "Not to me, no, but to Sam it seems it does. He's the youngest of seven. All his life he's had to put up with hand-me-downs and cast-offs.

"When we got married, his mum pleaded with me not to rush into anything, to let him be the centre of my world for a while. Now it looks like I'm expecting and in less than a year all my attention will be focused on a baby."

Claire stood up. "Okay, I've heard **Continued overleaf…**

"Three days!" Claire exclaimed, pouring on the freshly boiled water. "But that's nothing, surely?"

"It is for me," Polly told her. "Sam reckons I'm as regular as the tides."

Something in Polly's distinctly

enough ifs, buts and maybes for one day," she said, risking third-degree burns by downing her coffee in one. "First we have to find out if you really are pregnant. Come on, girl, get that down you and let's go and find a late night pharmacy."

It was well past eleven when Claire opened the door to her second caller that night. Sam Meadows stood on the doorstep, whey-faced in the moonlight.

"Sorry to disturb you, Claire," he said, "but Pol's late and I wondered if you knew anything about it."

Thank goodness, Claire thought with great relief, *he already knows*. Then it suddenly dawned on her; he was, of course, referring to the lateness of the by the fire. "For some reason she seems to have gone and changed her mind about us having any."

Claire scratched her head. Were these two actually in the same room when they talked to each other?

"When we married we agreed that we'd save up for a bit, get a few bob behind us, and then start a family. At least, that's what I thought we'd agreed. But she seems to have gone off the whole idea and I…"

"Sorry, Sam," Claire said, cutting across him, "but where did you get the notion from that she's changed her mind about having kids?"

"From her," he insisted. "This morning, right out of the blue, she suddenly asked

"For some reason she seems to have changed her mind about having kids"

hour and his wife's unexplained absence from their home.

"Come in," she sighed, standing back to let him pass.

Ducking his head, the six-foot-four-inch fireman manoeuvered his giant frame carefully along the hallway and into the lounge.

"I'm sorry to bother you," he repeated, self-consciously shifting his weight from one foot to the other, "I just wondered if she'd said anything to you about where she might be going. Only, we had a bit of a tiff this morning and, well, I know how you two talk."

That would be Pol, actually, Claire corrected him silently. "What was the disagreement about, Sam?" she asked, motioning for him to sit down.

"Children," he said forlornly, folding his huge frame into the saggy old armchair how important it was to me to stick to our plan for starting a family in three years. Well, of course I said as far as I was concerned it was very important."

"By which you meant that it's important that you start *within* three years?" Claire pressed.

"Yes," he agreed, plucking distractedly at a loose thread on the arm of the chair, "What else would it mean?"

"Well," she said carefully, "it could be taken to mean the exact opposite; that you want to delay it for at least that long and not start before three years."

"What? No," he cried, aghast. "This year, next year, I don't mind when they come, as long as they do. I'm one of seven kids, Claire. I grew up in a house full of noise and laughter. I can't wait to have that for us."

"So tell me, Sam, where did this three-

convinced herself that there being so many of us meant that we'd all lost out somehow, her and Dad included.

"She was already pregnant when they married, you see, so it's my guess she told Pol not to rush it, to let us live a bit first and get to know one another before we start a family.

"She means well but she forgets that we lived together for two years before we married. We know each other inside out."

Claire's mouth twitched wryly. *Or, quite possibly, not at all.*

"Would you excuse me for a minute, Sam?" she said. "There's something I want to check out."

Leaving him staring distractedly into the fire she hurried upstairs and tapped lightly on the bathroom door. "Polly, love, are you there?"

The door opened and Polly's sad face appeared in the gap.

"Well?" Claire asked briskly. "What's the verdict, then?"

"It's positive," Polly answered miserably, holding out the plastic strip with its double band of blue, "I'm definitely pregnant."

As Polly's eyes welled with tears, Claire reached out and took her by the hand.

"Come here, you," she said kindly, "and bring that test strip with you. There's someone waiting downstairs you have *got* to talk to..."

She thought a baby would create such a distance between them...

year plan come from exactly, if not from you?" Claire asked shrewdly.

"My mum," he replied ruefully. "She loved us all, no question, but she

A WORD FROM THE AUTHOR

"Confusing, upsetting, open to misinterpretation – the way we communicate can cause all sorts of problems. Fortunately for Polly and Sam, Claire was there to make sense of it all."

Love Among The Coffee Cups

You have to be able to forgive before you can move on –
but forgiveness is not always something you give to others

By Lydia Jones

A screech of steam shocks me from my seat. I settle, flicking furtive glances around the coffee shop to see if anyone noticed. This was where we met after work. Why did I agree to come?

The coffee machine growls on. I grip both hands around brown-crust dregs of my cup's cappuccino. I was way too early.

"I think we should talk it through," Mark had said. "What's the point in paying solicitors to send letters? Surely we can be civilised."

"I'll come round," I said.

"No, no – I think it should be on neutral ground, don't you?" His voice was crisp as a paper cut and I conceded.

survived that phase. It's supposed to be such a strain, isn't it? But somehow we just clicked into a groove.

Maybe the groove was too well-worn. I don't know any more. I'm wrung out searching for a reason.

It was when the kids were gone that the problems began. So trite – have all those years of loving been reduced to nothing more than a mid-life crisis cliché?

The music in here is all 1980s. Today it only makes me feel middle-aged.

At a corner table, a young couple sit barely a kiss apart. Inevitably memory brings me a late night in the student union; plastic cups and poisonous coffee, his blue eyes like swimming pools I so wanted to dive into.

"Let's go back to yours for a drink,"

Now he asks me here to pick through the pieces, but I don't know if I can do it

A blast of chill air announces a new customer. I look up, stomach swirling. False alarm. A woman with a double buggy struggles with the heavy door and shopping bags. I get up to hold it open and she shoots me an exhausted smile.

I remember those days. Funny how we

Mark had said, his crooked finger tracing the outline of my lips. I knew right then my life would never be the same.

Sometimes my life seems measured out in coffee moments. I drink way too much of the stuff.

I squeeze eyes tight shut against more

I'm wrung out searching for a reason…

recent images I so don't want my mind to find – fingers and feet entwined like that young couple's; long treacherous fingers cupping a face in adoration. So sleek, so young, so not like mine.

Did it begin in this coffee shop, that half-life of hotel rooms and snatched telephone conversations? And now he asks me here to pick through the pieces. I don't know if I can.

This time the door's draught does bring Mark. Hesitating, he scans the tables. I raise my hand the way I've done across a million rooms before. He smiles but it doesn't reach his eyes – they are stones that set me shivering in a way that has nothing to do with the autumn air. He looks grey, tired. It makes me sad.

I gesture and he sits, pulling his raincoat around him like a shield.

"I see you've already had…" He waves **Continued overleaf…**

a little indifferently at my empty cup.

"I'd still like another – you know me."
Stupid thing to say. He grins, and for a
moment hope hovers until a glance from
his stony eyes squash it.

"I'll go." He stands.

The young couple in the corner are
openly kissing – little pecks, polite
enough for a public place but laced with
so much love, it brings a rock to my chest.
Instinctively I look towards the counter
and Mark's back.

"You've lost weight." I tell him when he
returns to the table.

Perhaps this new situation suits him.
No. I don't want to think about that.

Across the years I see Southampton
university refectory, young boys playing

He clears his throat, obviously in
business manager mode.

I watch his mouth make words; my
ears bringing me phrases about furniture
and insurance policies. They fracture like
a splintered mirror in my mind, with each
shard tearing into me until I simply have
to make it stop.

"I spoke to Emma yesterday."

Our baby. Our beautiful daughter;
always her father's favourite, even though
he tried hard not to show it.

"I'm glad."

His face softens as I knew it would.

"I told her I was coming here today."

The boys have been pretty supportive
in that cuff-the-shoulder-we-don't-do-
physical-contact way that they still

My mind is too full of coffee moments from the life that's slipping away…

instruments on canteen tables, beer cans,
jeans, burgeoning youth and talent. I
don't need to say anything – Mark's eyes
tell me he's seeing it too.

"What are we going to do about the
record collection?" he blurts.

"You have it."

There's this metallic taste in my mouth.

"But some of the vinyl is quite valuable
now," he persists.

"I haven't got anything to play it on."

"I won't play it."

His voice unravels. Of course not. Too
many memories. And we're moving
forward now, aren't we?

The hand that reaches for his cup
shakes just a fraction and with everything
inside of me I long to fold it in my own;
feel the familiar contours of the rugby-
dislocated finger.

But he doesn't want that any more.

haven't grown out of. But Emma has been
completely bewildered, as if she felt
betrayed herself. My heart has ached to
make it better for her.

"She's a good girl," I say.

"I guess we did some things right."

"Lots of things…"

My gaze lingers, willing him to connect
with me again.

His eyes blink back a barrier.

He tries to pull us back to practicalities,
but I can't speak.

My mind is too full of coffee moments
from the life that's slipping away…

Mark at his computer, mobile
crammed between shoulder and cheek,
me passing the mug, his eyes flashing
irritation fudged with tiredness; coffees
on the run; cosy coffees snuggling on the
sofa with football on TV with me giggling
and saying mischievously, "Tell me again

We'd said enough sorries

his cup. The little crooked one curves towards the saucer. "But I want you to know it wasn't a conscious thing. I let it happen, I know. Even after Emma left and I saw you were floundering… I should have –"

"Doesn't matter. No excuse."

I don't seem able to form a sentence. My cheeks are wet with tears.

"I'm sorry Mark. I'm so, so sorry."

"Enough sorries."

His hand finds mine and I rub my fingers against the familiar scar.

"I'm taking early retirement."

"What?"

"I should have done it before – before…" I see his face shutting a door. "Years ago. It's a young man's game. It costs too much to keep up."

I'm not sure I'm still breathing.

"And that's… that's okay with you?"

"I'm not saying it's the answer to everything, Chrissie. But I guess it's a start and that's more than okay with me."

His eyes are faded now but still as large as swimming pools. They crinkle into a smile. His crooked finger traces damp tear tracks in my make-up.

"Now, drink your coffee before it goes cold," he tells me.

I cradle the still-warm cappuccino and smile back at my husband.

If Mark can forgive me for the affair then maybe I can begin to forgive myself.

Perhaps, after all, this will be one more momentous coffee moment.

why we need to watch it when you've already been to the match?"

Loss throbs in every sinew and when I look up Mark's mouth has stopped moving. It quivers.

"Chrissie – I don't want a divorce."

The air between us buzzes as I struggle to make words of my own.

"But what happened with…" I simply can't bring myself to say the name. "You said that…"

He sighs like all the breath he has is leaving his body.

"I know what I said. I was confused."

"So was I."

"But I've had time to think since then and I see now that we betrayed each other. Both of us."

There's this fizzing strand of hope winding its way around my stomach. I daren't speak or even move.

"I know you think I always put the job first." He stares at his own fingers next to

ILLUSTRATIONS: JOHN HANCOCK, JAMES DEWAR

A Home For Ginger

Hungry and alone, what will become of this timid kitten?
A heartwarming story for animal lovers everywhere…

By Georgie Foord

The kitten wriggled further back into his hiding place in the straw bales. All day he had been bombarded with terrifyingly loud noises from the yard outside the barn: men shouting, cows mooing in distress, dogs barking, lorries grinding in low gear in and out of the yard. But now it was all spookily quiet, with none of the normal early evening clatter of a busy working farm.

He missed the familiar sounds from the milking parlour: the clanking of metal machinery, the cheerful voice of Geoff the cowman as he walked his charges back to their pasture.

The kitten's family had been taken her wriggling, squeaking cargo.

"There's a couple of tortie girls here and a black and white male. Didn't the lady say there was a little ginger boy, too?"

The man was crouching on his haunches beside the basket, trying to calm the kittens' yowling and frantic mother. He straightened up and gazed around the cavernous barn.

"I'll try calling him," suggested Bev. "Here, kittykittykitty! Come on then!"

But the ginger kitten was far too scared to show himself to strangers, especially strangers who had imprisoned his mother.

"Um… well," said the man. "He's not around anywhere. Maybe he's found a home already? Marmalades are always popular. Anyway, best be off before Mum here goes completely bonkers."

"Here, kitty, kitty! Come on then!" But the kitten was too scared to show himself

away. He had watched from his hiding place, quaking with fear, as a man and woman in green uniforms had captured his mother, brother and sisters and secured them in wire carriers.

"How many've you got, Bev?" the man had asked. The young woman surveyed

And they had picked up the baskets and carefully carried the ginger kitten's family out of the barn.

Now it was evening. He was all alone, and very hungry. Summoning up his courage, he scrambled down the straw **Continued overleaf…**

Sweet

He couldn't understand why he'd been abandoned

Continued from previous page

The box was set down carefully on the pavement. "Bye then, Ginger," said the man. "You behave yourself now, okay?"

The kitten heard footsteps approaching, stopping near him. The box was lifted up; there were sounds of a key in a lock and a door opening, scrabbling noises on the box as the twine was cut away, then light suddenly flooding in. An elderly face peered down at him.

He sighed and clicked his tongue in exasperation. "So what am I going to do with you?" he said. "I can't have you here." He set the box down in the corner.

The shop door opened, jangling the

"Oh, what a beauty!" she exclaimed. "He won't be long finding a home."

The little girl had her own idea about a home for the ginger kitten. "Mummy, Mummy, couldn't I have him, pleeeese? For my very own? I did see him first, didn't I?" she begged.

"Oh Emily! How many more cats do you want, for goodness' sake? And how would he fit in with all our show cats?"

The shop owner winked at Emily. "Well, I don't suppose this little chap would make all that much difference, do you? And I am sure little Missy here could look after him all by herself, eh?"

The woman laughed. "Perhaps she

"I promise he'll be the bestest looked-after kitten ever – you'll see, Mummy!"

old-fashioned bell suspended above it. A young woman and her daughter came in and the child went to inspect the cages of small animals – gerbils, hamsters and mice. Her mother was at the counter, buying cans of cat food, a flea collar and other bits and pieces of cat paraphernalia.

The little girl wandered to the back of the shop and discovered the cardboard box. "Mummy!" she cried in delight. "Come and look!"

The shop owner sighed. "Found it dumped on the doorstep this morning," he said. "I can't have it here. The small cage pets, they're all right, but puppies and kittens – they don't belong in a shop. I suppose I'll have to take it to the shelter. So irresponsible, people dumping animals like that." Grumbling, he took the woman's money and counted out change.

The child pulled at her mother's hand. "Come and see, Mummy, he's so sweet!"

The woman gently lifted the kitten out.

could. Oh, all right – but Emily, he's your baby, you have to make sure he's fed – and do his litter tray!"

The child's eyes shone. "Course I will, Mummy. He'll be the bestest looked-after cat ever – you'll see!"

They walked out of the shop, Emily happily thinking up names. "I think I'll call him Gingernut, Mummy – or Rusty, or what about Marmalade?"

They didn't even glance at the young vagrant on the other side of the busy road. He bid a silent farewell to the ginger kitten, shouldered his backpack and turned away, satisfied.

A WORD FROM THE AUTHOR

"I have loved cats all my life and when an abandoned ginger kitten found his way to me, I felt I had to invent a history for him."

Teatime Treat

EASY TRAY BAKE

Honeycomb Sweetie Cake

Ingredients
- 150g (5oz) unsalted butter
- 450g (1lb) milk chocolate, broken into chunks
- 150g (5oz) Malted Milk biscuits, crushed into small pieces
- 100g (3½oz) sultanas
- 75g (3oz) mini marshmallows
- 150g (5oz) honeycomb, lightly crushed

To Decorate
- Hundreds and thousands

CHOC & FUN!

Preparation time: 20mins plus cooling and chilling
Cooking time: 5mins
Makes 36

- Line a 20cm (8inch) square cake tin with cling film. Put **butter** and **milk chocolate** in a saucepan over a very low heat to melt. Stir occasionally, then set aside to cool for 10mins. Meanwhile, put **biscuits**, **sultanas** and **mini marshmallows** in a bowl, and stir in the **honeycomb**.
- Spoon the melted chocolate mixture over the dry ingredients and mix well to thoroughly coat everything. Pile into prepared tin and press down well. Sprinkle with **hundreds and thousands**. Cover loosely and chill for about 2hrs until firm and set.
- To serve, carefully remove the chocolate cake from the tin and discard the cling film. Using a large, sharp knife, cut in 6 thin slices one way; quarter turn and cut in 6 slices in the other direction to make 36 small cubes.

RECIPES/STYLING: KATHRYN HAWKINS PHOTOGRAPHY: LIGHTHOUSE PHOTOGRAPHY

Treats In Store

Has Carla, the diet enthusiast, gone too far? Or will she realise in time to keep gorgeous Gavin's affections?

By Sandra Woolfenden

G avin gasped in horror. "Whatever are you doing?"

"Emptying the cupboards of everything we aren't allowed to eat," Carla answered piously. "If we want to lose a few pounds before Christmas, it's the only way."

"You can't throw out packets of biscuits!" Gavin said. "That's plain crazy."

"But I'm doing it for you, love. That's your trigger food."

"My what?"

"Trigger food – your weakness."

"The odd biscuit won't do me any harm," Gavin objected.

"Ah, but that's what I mean. It's never just an odd biscuit – before you even know it, you've eaten half the packet."

Her weight loss was a steady one to two pounds a week. She was walking more instead of taking the car, ignoring the lift and running up the stairs to her third floor office. Gavin complained she was like someone who had just found religion and wanted to convert everyone else.

"It's for your own good!" she told him.

She'd been about to complain that the biscuit tin was getting low and they'd had no visitors, but thought better of it. What she'd do with the new packet of "visitors' biscuits" was to hide them. But where?

She'd planned something special for their evening meal.

"Mmm! That smells good," Gavin complimented her.

"Stir fry," she told him. By then she'd hidden the chocolate digestives, in a place where he'd never think of looking.

What she had to do with the new packet of "visitors' biscuits" was hide them!

"Now you're just exaggerating."

"Only a little. Be honest."

"You can't throw out all the biscuits. What about when we have visitors?"

"All right," Carla conceded. "We'll have a tin of biscuits for visitors."

Carla was well pleased with herself.

"You're looking great," he told her. She knew it was an apology for his earlier outburst, which she showed with a kiss that she accepted.

The meal had taken a bit of effort but she was sure it would be worth it. She'd added aubergine to the meat so she could

**It should be easy
to save treats for
visitors…**

use less and cut the calories; next, she'd added onions and a generous mix of chopped fresh vegetables. It looked colourful and appetising.

"It doesn't taste right," said Gavin.

"Different," she admitted, "but tasty."

"I wouldn't go that far. What have you done, exactly?"

"I fried it all in half a stock cube."

"You can't 'fry' in a stock cube. You need oil, love."

"It's healthy and it's very low calorie."

"It doesn't taste right and I can't eat it!"

While she was wondering if she should take his plate and empty it over his head, **Continued overleaf…**

he added, "I'm going to get a takeaway."

She was too upset to eat her tea. By the time he came home she'd thrown the lot in the bin and locked herself in the bathroom, letting the water from the shower wash away her tears.

When Gavin came to bed she pretended to be asleep.

"This is ridiculous, Carla," he whispered. He kissed her shoulder, but she didn't turn to him as she would have done normally. With a sigh, he turned away so that both of them were lying apart, on the opposite edges of the bed.

certainly have to be a bit more subtle.

They'd married five years ago, when she was only nineteen and he just a couple of years older. She'd been very slim then, and Gavin was lean and muscular. So what had happened?

She was still wondering as she drank her coffee in the morning break at work. At twenty-four she could hardly put it down to middle-aged spread, but their lifestyle was different.

They'd met at the skating rink, she recalled; he'd been whizzing around and bumped into her and they'd both ended

"Gavin wouldn't mind me going line dancing. But it won't help him, will it?"

In the morning she was up earlier than usual. "It's only half past six," Gavin mumbled sleepily.

"I thought I'd get up and cook you a fry-up, something high cholesterol and fattening," she said sarcastically.

She was treading dangerously. He'd be angry, and any moment now they'd be having a full-blown argument. Whatever was she doing? She loved him, but before they knew it they'd be heading for divorce. What was the point of being a size ten if she hadn't got Gavin?

To her amazement he laughed. "I'm sorry about last night – but it was awful."

She laughed too and it was a wonderful relief. "You're not really fat, Gavin."

"Okay, I know I'm a little overweight. But giving up biscuits should be enough to sort it, don't you think?"

She could have asked him to explain how there were so few biscuits in the tin, but instead she slid back into bed, into his arms. She wasn't going to entirely give up on Gavin eating healthily – but she'd

up on the ice. If he hadn't been so good-looking, she might have been annoyed.

Wrapped up in a thick woolly scarf and gloves, she'd stood freezing on the sidelines to cheer him on in the local football team. Now, though, he spent more time watching footie on the box. They didn't go skating any more; it was more teenage, somehow, and to be honest she'd never been much good at it.

What about dancing? Carla didn't think she'd have much chance of getting Gavin to go to ballroom lessons with her.

"Your coffee will get cold. You're miles away," observed Leanne at the next desk.

"Just thinking…" Carla told her how she'd done a stir-fry without using oil, how Gavin hadn't appreciated it, and how they both needed more exercise.

"I go line dancing at least once a week. It's great fun. You could always join me," Leanne suggested.

"It's just not Gavin," Carla sighed.

"There aren't many men who go," Leanne admitted. "But you could still

"No, you don't! They're your trigger food"

If Leanne thought he was hunky rather than fat, maybe other girls would too

come along – make it a girls' night out."

"I'd love to, and Gavin wouldn't mind me going. But it won't help him, will it?"

"Gavin's not fat," Leanne told her. "More hunky."

Carla smiled. "I was thinking about the first time we met, skating. I thought he was really something. He told me weeks later he'd bumped into me on purpose so he had an excuse to speak to me.

"I guess I still fancy him as much now as I did then. Perhaps I'll just have to give up on his diet – well, I'll still try and cook carefully – but not make drastic changes."

And the biscuits, she thought. *I'll still try and restrict those, keep them hidden.*

Her phone rang. It was Gavin. "I won't be coming straight home this evening, Carla. Is that okay?"

"Sure," she answered pleasantly. "I'll see you when I see you."

She hadn't asked him why, or where he was going, she realised as she put the phone down.

A sudden surge of fear engulfed her. She'd been a bit of a pain since she'd got dieting fever. Maybe Gavin had had enough! Leanne was right, he was a hunk. And if Leanne saw him that way, then other girls might feel the same; girls in his office, for instance, who wouldn't infer he **Continued overleaf…**

Continued from previous page

was too fat, and would like him as he was.

With a great effort, she forced her mind back to her work.

O n the way home, she called into the supermarket and bought a joint of beef. It wouldn't hurt, for once, to have a few roast potatoes. She didn't want some other girl enticing him with roast dinners, now, did she?

She was being silly, she scolded herself as she unpacked her shopping. Just because he was going to be late and Leanne had pointed out he was a hunk. She mustn't be so insecure. He loved her. He'd never given her any reason to think otherwise, had he?

Most couples started out loving each other, though. So why didn't they all stay together? When did everything change? Was it when one of them became too

She didn't want some other girl enticing him

Carla set the table and switched on the oven to heat up. Then she heard Gavin's key in the lock and ran down the hall to meet him. "Sweetheart! You're earlier than I thought."

"I've been to play squash. Borrowed some shorts and a racquet from Tony at work, thoroughly enjoyed it, so I thought

Gavin walked into the kitchen just as she opened the oven door and gave a shriek

critical and forced their partner to seek reassurance elsewhere?

So where *was* Gavin this evening? She hadn't asked what time he'd be home. Of course she could ring his mobile but if he was with this girl from the office he might have switched it off – or worse, he'd cover the mouthpiece and tell her, "It's my wife; she's so possessive, wants to check on my every move."

No, she wouldn't ring; she'd make the meal reasonably late so it wouldn't get spoilt. And she'd just have to hope that he hadn't already eaten.

She'd indulge in a glass of wine to help her unwind. If she opened a bottle, they could have the rest with their meal.

I might get a racquet of my own and play every week. What do you think?"

"That's brilliant!" she told him happily.

The oven had reached the right temperature and she opened it to put in the roast. Gavin came into the kitchen as she gave a shriek. Looking at the gooey mess, she remembered where she'd hidden the chocolate biscuits!

A WORD FROM THE AUTHOR

"I once hid away some chocolate biscuits in case we had visitors as they disappear so quickly. I forgot about them until it was too late!"

Fancy That!

Totally 80s facts that make you go "Wow!"

Movie Hits

The Top Five box office smashes of the 80s were *ET*, *Return Of The Jedi*, *The Empire Strikes Back*, *Indiana Jones and The Last Crusade*, and *Batman*

● **The 1980s began on a Tuesday.**

● Among the chocolate bars launched in the 80s were Drifter (1980), Aero Chunky (1982), Wispa (1983), Boost (1985) and Inspirations (1989).

● **Michael Jackson's middle name was Joseph.**

● IBM launched its first PC in 1981.

WOW! ● **The first Girl Guide postage stamp was issued in 1982.**

● Canada gained official independence from Britain on April 17, 1982.

● **The Mary Rose was raised in 1982, 437 years after she sank in the Solent in 1545.**

● The Roman numerals for 1980 are MCMLXXX.

WOW! ● **The first Post-It notes were used in 1980 by their co-inventor Art Fry, a choir singer who used them as bookmarks in his music books.**

● 1987 saw Britain hit by the worst storm since the Great Storm of 1703.

● **3D computer graphics were invented by James Clark in 1984 and used that year in *Star Wars*.**

● Australia's worst ever bush fire killed 72 people on February 16, 1983, which became known as Ash Wednesday.

Fact!
EastEnders made its debut on February 19, 1985

Soaps Down Under
Kylie Minogue appeared in Australian soaps *The Sullivans*, *Skyways* and *The Hendersons* before finding fame as Charlene in *Neighbours*, in 1985

The Best Auntie In The World!

There's something very odd about Aunt Vicki – and you'll never guess what she has in store for Mark's birthday

By Sandra Beswetherick

A s Mark raced home from the sports field he was surprised to find his aunt standing on the corner at the end of his street. "Aunt Vicki! What are you doing here?" he asked, breathless from running.

The question seemed to puzzle his aunt. She cast about as if for an answer. As soon as her attention focused on him, though, her furrowed brow smoothed and her smile was dazzling. "I'm here to see you," she said happily, bending towards him. "Of course I am."

Mark extended his arms to hug her, but she threw up her hands and drew back out of reach. It was her smart cream-coloured suit, he thought. Made of linen

glanced over his shoulder, back the way he'd come. "Where's your mum?"

This question, especially when whispered, usually meant that Aunt Vicki was considering a plan of which his mum wouldn't approve.

"I don't mind that Vicki's well-off," Mum often said. "But why must she flaunt her wealth? Why must she constantly go against my wishes?"

His mum would invariably follow these questions with a disappointed sigh. "Sometimes I wonder if she really cares about our feelings at all."

His mum would feel differently if she knew about the teddy-bear charm she'd given Aunt Vicki for her charm bracelet years ago. The bracelet wasn't fashionable any more, according to his

Mum hated the way her well-off sister would sweep in with expensive gifts

or silk, or some other expensive fabric. His aunt could afford the best.

"Sorry, Aunt Vicki." He'd been playing football with a few of his mates and his hands were undeniably dirty.

"Not to worry," his aunt said, smiling and leaning towards him again. She then

aunt, but she still wore the charm against her heart on a length of gold chain. It was Aunt Vicki's secret, for whatever reason – and one that Mark kept.

"Mum and Kayley are already at the sports field setting up for my party. Some of the other parents are helping. Mum

He was surprised to see her so early

forgot the paper plates, so she sent me back to get them."

A frown of concentration wrinkled his aunt's forehead, as if she were trying to remember something important. She sometimes forgot, or let herself forget, the details of Mum's arrangements. She straightened now and peered in the direction he pointed. Obviously she couldn't see the field from here. "The sports field next to the rail lines," she said, as though reminding herself.

"Yeah. Mum booked it for my birthday.

The headmaster's refereeing our game. She's got sandwiches, cake, and ice-cream for after."

His mum couldn't afford the expensive birthday parties other parents threw for their offspring and Mark had lots of friends he wanted included. So they'd hit upon this idea.

"Your thirteenth birthday," Aunt Vicki said. That his aunt seemed to be fitting these bits of information together like pieces to a puzzle made Mark uneasy. **Continued overleaf…**

"That's right – and you were coming by train to help me celebrate. Mum was to fetch you from the station when the train arrived and bring you back to the party."

"At two o'clock," Aunt Vicki said, staring off into the distance. "Mark," she asked, "what time is it now?"

"That's the reason I asked why you were here. Your train's not due for another…" He glanced at the awesome, indestructible wristwatch she'd given him on his last birthday. "Twenty minutes."

A small gasp of surprise escaped his aunt. "Really?" She glanced round, eyes wide, and seemed to marvel at everything she saw. "Twenty minutes. There's time enough, then."

"Aunt Vicki," Mark blurted. His aunt's strange behaviour was creeping him out. "Are you all right?"

"Don't I look all right?" she asked, her eyes warm and loving, though perhaps a little sad. *Why sad?* he wondered. But she twirled round, arms extended, as she often did when modelling a new outfit, and this familiar action reassured him.

weekend trip to Disneyland Paris!

"Vicki! I thought we'd keep things simple," his mum would protest. Mark had overheard his mum telling a friend that sometimes Aunt Vicki made her feel inadequate as a mother. Which Mark knew wasn't true.

"Ah, Caroline, what's an aunt for if she can't spoil her niece and nephew on occasion?" Vicki would smile indulgently.

He and Kayley would sit not saying a word as Aunt Vicki and their mum confronted each other. Their eyes begged *please,* though. And at length their mum, with an exaggerated roll of her eyes, almost always relented.

"You've got to hurry, Mark," his aunt urged him now. "Run back down to the sports field and tell all your mates and your mum. The community hall. Two o'clock. That's when it starts – and everyone's got to be there."

"I dunno. Mum won't be pleased. She has everything ready."

His aunt bent to him again and the brush of her finger against his cheek was

"Two o'clock, it starts – everyone's got to be there. It'll be the best gift ever"

"And I'm here as part of my surprise."

Mark's heart lurched between sinking and soaring. His mum was rarely impressed by Aunt Vicki's surprises, while he and his sister couldn't help being thrilled by them.

Not that his mum's parties and gifts weren't special. It was just that, sometimes, his aunt swept in like a fairy godmother with presents his mum couldn't afford; MP3 players, the newest computer games. She might treat them to dinner at a posh restaurant… or even a

so light and soft, he wondered if he'd actually felt it. Her blue eyes were earnest. "I'm counting on you to convince them. You wouldn't want your favourite aunt disappointed."

Aunt Vicki gave him a playful pout. "Just tell them how great my surprises are. This will be the best gift ever, you'll see. Anyone who doesn't come…"

Her eyes softened suddenly. "Tell your mum it will only be for a short while. Then, afterwards, everyone can go back to the sports field."

Mark had invited all his friends

"Why does she do this to me?" his mum demanded, turning away, her back rigid, her hands clenched, once Mark had explained. He'd been right about her not being pleased. "I thought we'd agreed this time. Doesn't she care about my feelings?"

"Please, Mum. It's really important to Aunt Vicki. She said so."

"And this isn't important to me?" She threw up her hands. "The best gift ever? Give me a break."

But his mates had crowded round. They knew Aunt Vicki's reputation, had seen the gifts she'd given him and Kayley.

"What do you think she's arranged?" one girl asked eagerly.

Mark shrugged. "With Aunt Vicki, it's hard to tell." Which spiked their curiosity as Mark knew it would. His mum was outvoted, and had to take her car because there weren't enough to transport everyone otherwise.

Yet when they arrived at the hall it was empty, the front door locked, and at one minute to two there was no sign of his aunt.

"Is this a joke?" one boy asked. Mark turned to his mum, not knowing what to say. She was standing perfectly still, staring at something on the top step.

A horrendous bang, just then, shook the ground underfoot, rattled windows. It evolved into a scream of tearing metal and an unbelievable roar that seemed to go on forever. Everyone cowered instinctively, hands clapped over ears.

When the roar finally died, the silence was worse. A dark grey cloud drifted over the far end of town. "Oh, no," a dad whispered. "Train accident."

Three rail cars littered the sports field when they returned. Long furrows marked the turf where the derailed cars of Aunt Vicki's train had ploughed into the ground. The football nets were gone, the stands reduced to matchsticks.

Their mum drew Mark and Kayley close. "Best gift ever," she whispered. Then she began to cry.

Dangling from Mum's hand was the object from the step of the community hall that had drawn her attention. A teddy bear charm on a length of gold chain.

A WORD FROM THE AUTHOR

"This story began as a 'what if?' What if the bond between two sisters was so strong, the spirit of one sister could travel through space and time to save the lives of the ones she loved?"

In The Bleak Midwinter

This tale of a city mum adjusting to the challenges of life on the snow-covered moors will warm your heart

By Valerie Bowes

he glittering silvered landscape wouldn't have looked out of place on a Christmas card – and Amanda wished that's where it had stayed.

Beautiful it might be, but she hadn't been prepared for its impact on life in a small village in Yorkshire. January snow in south-east London was a rare opportunity for sledging bumpily down the sparse coverlet of white in the park, until it disappeared and the grass turned to mud. Here, as she looked up at the sloping hills from the school gates, the deep, unbroken sheet would have made

these." She stuck out a foot shod in thick leather with a sheepskin lining.

"I shall." Amanda was beginning to learn that fashion should be kept strictly for visits to town.

"Your Gordon back tonight, then?"

"Provided he's not snowed in. Have you heard what it's like in Harrogate?"

Tracey pulled a face. "Not good. Still, you'll be all right, won't you? Got plenty of grub in? Send your Charlie down to ours if you need anything."

"Oh, we'll be fine," Amanda said, with a hint of pride. The other mothers had warned her to keep her cupboards well stocked, and she'd seen the sense in it, even if it wasn't something she'd ever

Gordon might not be home. At least she had taken the advice to stock up on food

Good King Wenceslas feel right at home.

"All right?" Tracey appeared by her side, pulling a woollen scarf tighter around her ears. "Hope Mrs Holton lets 'em go a bit early. It's fair freezing today."

Amanda shivered. "I think my feet are about to drop off."

Tracey shot a sideways glance at Amanda's slim, fashionable boots.

"Get yourself some tractor tyres like

had to do before their move here.

The children spilled out noisily into the snowy playground.

"Hey, our Mam, can Charlie come to tea?" A little lad, red-haired like his mother, tugged at Tracey's coat.

Tracey shook her head. "Not tonight, Kev. Charlie needs to take care of his mum this evening. I reckon it's going to

Continued overleaf...

She and
Charlie were
learning fast

snow again. If there's another heavy fall, school'll be closed tomorrow."

The boys cheered, and were soon enjoying a running snowball fight as they walked home.

Tracey and Kevin bade them goodbye at the bottom of the lane. "Don't forget, now," Tracey admonished. "You need owt, you call us, right?"

"Thanks." Amanda smiled. "I will."

Mum, what does vunnable mean?" Charlie asked as they settled down to their tea in the warm kitchen. "Mrs Holton says we must keep an eye out for vunnable people while the snow's here, and help them. Does she mean Fred? I helped him out with the sheep in the summer, didn't I?"

Amanda smiled. She could think of no one less vulnerable than the sturdy farmer and his practical, capable wife.

"Not that sort of help. She means people like… like…" Now she came to think of it, she couldn't name anyone in the village that came into the vulnerable category. They'd all been coping with

"She must be about a hundred, and she lives right up on the moor."

Amanda had forgotten about Edith Pendleton. She wasn't quite as ancient as she must seem from Charlie's eight-year-old perspective, but she was certainly getting on. Amanda had met her in the village store, and seen her carrying her purchases up the long incline that led past their own house and onto the moor. She had no car and from what Mary, who ran the shop, had said in passing, her house had few modern conveniences.

"I expect she's used to winters like this," Amanda said, trying to convince herself as well as her son.

"Can't you phone, to see if she's okay?" Charlie urged.

"I could try, after tea, if she's in the phone book," Amanda said doubtfully. She'd only spoken to Edith once or twice. How would the independent old lady feel about being rung up by a comparative stranger; a soft Southerner who'd only been here five minutes? Would she be pleased – or insulted? In this close-knit community, Edith was

Their old neighbour might see a soft Southerner's concern as interference

severe weather since their cradles.

"Like Ethel Barnes," she said at last, thinking of their neighbour in Catford.

"You used to get her shopping," Charlie remembered. "And took her dinner in to her sometimes. Perhaps there's someone like that here?"

"If anyone needs us, we'll help," she promised. Charlie nodded and began to eat as though he'd starved for a week.

"What about Miss Pendleton?" he said suddenly, through a mouthful of cake.

bound to have friends and family to look out for her. She might well see Amanda's concern as unwarranted interference.

When she tried the phone, it was dead.

"I expect the snow's brought down the lines over the moor," she told Charlie.

"Wouldn't she have a mobile?"

"I doubt it," Amanda said, unable to repress a smile. "But if she has, I don't know the number. I just hope your dad can get through on his."

She guessed before he rang that

They had a running snowball fight as they walked home

Gordon would not be able to get home this evening.

"I'm really sorry, Manda." The anxiety in his voice was like a warm blanket. "Maybe I shouldn't have taken this job. You're a city girl. I shouldn't have expected you to cope with being stuck out in the sticks on your own."

She laughed. "Oh, get on with you. I may not be Yorkshire born and bred like you, but I love it here and I'm learning to be a real countrywoman. I'd rather you stayed put, where I know you're safe, than have an accident trying to get back."

"Well, stay safe yourself. Don't go out unless you have to, and keep warm."

"We're not going anywhere tonight," she assured him.

Tracey knew her weather. Amanda drew back the curtains as usual when Charlie was in bed, and found the sky flowing with fat white flakes again.

"If this goes on all night, there won't be any school in the morning," she said, and Charlie grinned sleepily up at her.

"We could go and see if Miss Pendleton's okay, couldn't we, Mum?"

"We'll see," she temporised, not wanting to get drawn into discussing impossibilities. But the thought of the old lady marooned behind a growing wall of white haunted her dreams.

The switch clicked uselessly when Amanda went to put on the light the next morning. "Oh dear. The power's off," she said unnecessarily.

"There'll be no school, then," Charlie observed cheerfully.

But Amanda was worried. The power must have gone off fairly early during the night, for the boiler was lifeless and the radiators barely warm. Charlie spooned up his cornflakes and drank fruit-juice with relish, but Amanda longed for a hot **Continued overleaf...**

cup of tea. Still, the electricity would be back on soon.

But it remained stubbornly off. Still, there was always the stove, wasn't there?

She glared at the wood-burning stove in active dislike. Gordon and Tracey both had the knack of lighting it and keeping it burning, but, no matter how hard they tried to impart the knowledge to Amanda, the stove always defeated her.

Well, it wasn't going to now, when she really needed it. Despite the jumpers they'd piled on, Charlie's nose looked pinched with cold.

She used up all the firelighters but, for all the good they did, she might just as well have thrown them into the snow.

"What else can I use?" she murmured, giving the stove an angry slap. "It needn't think it's going to win!"

"Kev's mum uses scrumpled newspaper," Charlie offered.

"Okay, team, find me some newspaper!"

Although Amanda didn't think that anything so dramatic had happened, the thought Charlie had implanted niggled away at her conscience. Whatever her shortcomings with the fire, she was young, fit and active. Edith Pendleton was old and looked about as tough as a dandelion puff.

"Look, Mum!" Charlie said suddenly. "It's going."

The flame was definitely stronger now. It climbed up and waved rosily from behind the glass as Amanda carefully shut the door.

"Right, you," she said, waving a finger. "Don't you dare go out."

It didn't. Soon, a comforting warmth was creeping through the kitchen.

"Wonder if Miss Pendleton likes hot chocolate?" Charlie said, elaborately thoughtful as he sipped at his mug.

"Let's go and see, shall we?" Amanda said, as if her victory over the stove had

Tears stung her eyes as the stove failed again to light. Who was she kidding?

Charlie knelt beside her as the small flame wavered and dimmed. Tears of frustration stung her eyes. Learning to be a real countrywoman, was she? Who was she kidding?

Charlie was still fretting about Miss Pendleton. "We're supposed to look after vunnable people. Mrs Holton said so."

"I know, love, but there's not a lot we can do. I can't even light the fire," Amanda said, furious with herself.

"But you've got me," he pointed out. "She hasn't got anyone. S'pose she's slipped in the ice? S'pose she's lying there, without anyone to help?"

"Honestly, you and your imagination!"

lit another sort of fire. "Do you think you can walk that far in all this snow?"

Charlie looked his disgust at her question, so she unearthed some rolls from the freezer, hoping fervently that the electricity would be put back on before everything in it defrosted. With the rolls and a couple of tins of ham in a rucksack, they set off, bundled up like a couple of Michelin men.

The snow was even thicker than Amanda had thought, and got deeper the higher they went. Pausing for a breather, she looked down the sweep of the valley and thought she'd never seen anything so lovely – or so potentially deadly.

it, love? I were bringing you a bit of stew. I thought you might be finding it a bit hard, like, with them power lines down again."

"How did you cook it, then?" Charlie demanded as Amanda stammered her thanks.

"Oh, I've got the old range. Cooks a rare stew, does that." She cast a knowledgeable eye over them both. "You look frozen to the bone. Come on up to ours and have something to warm you up."

The farmhouse might look as if it had been marooned in the 1940s, but it was homely, comfortable and as warm as toast. Amanda curled her hands around a mug of steaming tea and wiggled her toes in front of the glowing range while Edith stuffed newspaper into her sodden boots to dry them.

"I don't think she's vunnable, do you, Mum?" Charlie whispered, polishing off a thickly buttered slice of rich fruit loaf. "This is wicked cake."

No, Amanda thought. *We were the vulnerable ones.*

But not any longer. The very first opportunity she got, she'd buy them all some decent boots and next winter she'd be able to cope as well as anyone. And with neighbours like Edith and Tracey to look out for them, what had they got to worry about?

They'd be absolutely fine.

Her boots were wet through, but Charlie was forging on with determination. The house on the lonely moor seemed to be always around the next bend or over the next rise. Surely, it wasn't this far?

Amanda started to fret that they had lost their way. She stopped, looking back to reassure herself that she could still see their footprints, leading back the way they had come. *If it starts to snow, we'll have to go back while we can still see them,* she thought, tugging down her hood against the spiteful, stinging wind that had sprung up.

She was trying to extricate a highly amused Charlie from a particularly deep drift when she heard the call.

"Hey up! You having trouble?"

Amanda looked up, and saw Edith coming down the field towards them, crunching merrily through the snow in waterproofs and wellies.

"You're Miss Pendleton," Charlie announced. "We were coming to see if you were all right."

"By, were you?" Edith winked at him. "That's right kind of you, lad. Happen we were thinking along the same lines. I were coming to see you!" She turned to Amanda. "It's your first winter here, isn't

A WORD FROM THE AUTHOR

"The woodburning stove in our holiday cottage simply would not stay alight. I wondered how it would be if it had been winter and we really needed it."

All I Want For Christmas

Let this tale of a little girl's simple Christmas wish, amidst her mother's frantic preparations, warm your heart…

By Ann Cartlidge

The plump man with the white beard set pink, pudgy hands on his red-clad knees, bent forward inquiringly and said, "So, what do you want for Christmas?"

Tracey patted her daughter's shoulder. "Come on, Sarah Jane. Tell Father Christmas what you want."

Sarah looked up at her and beckoned. Tracey shot an apologetic glance at Father Christmas and squatted so that her ear was on a level with Sarah's mouth as she whispered urgently.

"It isn't him," Sarah hissed. "Can we go to another one?"

Tracey sighed. "We've been to three already, and it's costing me a fortune. Just tell him what you want, there's a

a hunted look at Father Christmas, accepted a small wrapped gift and shot thankfully out of the North Pole Grotto.

North Pole Grotty, more like, she thought as Sarah towed her out of the store. *How they have the cheek to charge the prices they do, I don't know.*

A few cut-out fir trees sprayed with glitter-dust, a tangle of tinsel, a cotton-wool beard and a cardboard sleigh; it was hardly likely to reinforce wavering belief in the existence of a jolly old man who brought presents at Christmas.

And she really didn't want Sarah to lose that belief just yet. Not at seven years old. Let her hang onto this small bit of childhood magic for a little longer, she prayed silently. They lose it quickly enough as it is.

"Couldn't we go to Spencer's?" Sarah

Tracey didn't want Sarah to lose her belief in Santa just yet, not at only seven

love." *And then we can go home and sit down*, her mind added wearily.

"Look, it's nearly five o'clock and there's a queue a mile long out there," Father Christmas complained rather grumpily. "Let's get on with it, shall we?"

But Sarah shook her head. Tracey cast

asked as they emerged onto the street where reflections from the Christmas lights made rainbows in the puddles.

Tracey looked at her watch. "Not today. It's too far to go now. You've got a rehearsal in an hour's time, don't forget."
Continued overleaf…

There were six
little angels
in a row

"Then can we go tomorrow? Please, Mummy?" Sarah pleaded.

"We'll see. Come on, I'm dying for a cup of tea before we go to your play."

The brightly lit church hall was full of sheep and shepherds. A Wise Man was complaining that he didn't know where his frankincense was and Joseph was poking the donkey with his staff.

Linda McIntosh looked down from the stepladder, pointing with the shimmering star in her hand.

"Tracey, dear, could you...?"

Tracey went to rescue the donkey before he could retaliate, while Sarah dodged through the cast to join her fellow angels. Angel Gabriel, being older and

"No, they won't. They'll go aaaah!" Tracey said. "Anyway, Sarah's okay and Sonia's got a full set, haven't you, Sonia?"

The Angel Gabriel displayed her ten-year-old teeth with relish. Linda forced a smile and agreed, but Tracey knew how much this Nativity play meant to her. It was the first time she'd taken on the responsibility and she wanted it to be perfect. She hadn't bargained on angels looking more like mini Draculas.

If Tracey thought Sarah had forgotten about going to see Spencer's Father Christmas, she was wrong. It would be the same as all the others, she thought, as they made their way to the old shop on the outskirts of the town.

At first sight, she was right. The Grotto

The angel Gabriel fastened wings while a Wise Man searched for frankincense

bigger, was helping to fasten wings and halos by the time Tracey had persuaded Joseph to stand his staff in the corner until it was needed.

"Not another one!" She couldn't help laughing as she saw five gap-toothed grins, but Linda was feeling frazzled.

"They were all fine when we started rehearsing. That makes three in the last week," she said. "Why now?"

The smallest angel wiggled her tongue through the hole where her front tooth had been until this morning.

"My mum says the Tooth Fairy'll leave a pound under my pillow," she lisped.

"There's inflation for you!" Tracey said. "Used to be fifty pee."

"Used to be sixpence," Linda snorted. "Never mind the going rate for teeth, what am I going to do about my angels? Everyone'll laugh."

had obviously seen better days, but the original designer had shown some imagination and the store had at least kept it in good repair. Neither were there too many in front of them in the queue, as Tracey was pleased to see. She was getting very bored with standing in line to see a Father Christmas.

When it was their turn, a smiling elf dressed in red and green ushered them through the glistening icicles that formed the gates. Sarah gasped as they saw Father Christmas awaiting them.

"Mummy, it's him!" she whispered.

Even with the cynical eye of adulthood, Tracey could see why Sarah considered this to be the real deal. The luxurious beard tumbled in snowy waves over a capacious chest, the lips beneath it curved in a genuine smile. Cuddly and cordial, this Father Christmas owed

There were excited preparations for the Nativity

that?" Honestly, men!

"We've spent as much as we can afford, Tracey. If she's after whatever's the latest must-have to be like her mates, I'm afraid she'll be disappointed," Pete warned.

Things were tight. Tracey knew it. What was this thing that Sarah was so desperate to have that she was prepared to drag round every grotto in town? Whatever it was, to Tracey's dismay, Sarah was only telling Father Christmas. She could just make out the urgent murmur of the whispered request, but nothing more.

"I think we might manage that, Sarah Jane." Father Christmas beamed down into Sarah's uplifted face and gave a conspiratorial wink. Tracey saw a small shower of glittering silver dust descend from the wintry crown, leaving sparkles in her daughter's hair.

"Thank you, Father Christmas," Sarah said as Tracey had taught her, but this time the thanks were fervent and sincere.

"Just wait for me outside for a sec." Tracey pushed Sarah gently through the door and turned back quickly. "Can you

nothing to padding or cotton-wool and, instead of the usual red cap trimmed with a dangling pompom and tired lint, he wore a glittering garland of silvered holly and ivy leaves.

"Come and tell me what you want," he invited in a voice that made Tracey think of dark, rich hot chocolate and crackling log fires. Sarah went straight up to him and he bent his head.

Tracey had been waiting with impatience for Sarah to tell her wish. The

Tracey was getting bored standing in line to see yet another Father Christmas

days were ticking past. Christmas would be here before they knew it. There wasn't much time left in which to add to the presents safely hidden away from inquisitive eyes.

"Couldn't you just ask her?" Pete had suggested one evening.

"Do you think I haven't already done

tell me what she asked for, please?"

Father Christmas shook his head. "Ah, now, don't you worry about that. You just leave it to me."

Tracey stared at him. Wasn't that taking things a bit far? He of all people should know that it was down to the **Continued overleaf…**

Continued from previous page

parents to make the wishes come true.

"Come on, Mummy," Sarah called. Father Christmas nodded, smiling, and Tracey had no alternative but to go. It wasn't until she was in bed beside a softly snoring Pete that it occurred to her to wonder how Father Christmas had known Sarah's name.

The last few days of the pre-Christmas rush whizzed by in a welter of things to do and places to be. School had broken up amid a riot of revelry. Tracey only had the last-minute items of food to get – and, of course, Sarah's wish.

But she still didn't know what it was. Sarah wasn't saying, but she seemed as if she would burst with anticipation and Tracey was getting more and more anxious. Her daughter would be so disappointed on Christmas Day. She'd think Father Christmas had failed her.

What was Sarah's special wish?

Christmas. He kept his promise – and just in time." And she showed Tracey what was nestling in her palm.

Tracey plumped into a chair next to Pete as the curtain swished back. The spotlight shone brightly on the winged Gabriel. But it was the attendant angels, tinsel haloes sparking glints of Christmas

"I told you he was real. Father Christmas kept his promise – and just in time!"

The church hall was buzzing with expectancy. Tracey helped to settle stripy tea-towels on the shepherds' heads, herd the sheep into position and find the frankincense again.

It was time to make her escape from the crowded area back-stage and make her way to the front so she could watch the ancient story unfold. She looked around for the angels, to wish them luck. They were in a huddle, heads bent, behind a fence of wings.

Oh no! What had gone wrong now? She pushed her way over.

Sarah looked up, her face shining.

"I told you it was the real Father

glory, who caused the stir among the assembled parents and friends. As one, they grinned at the audience; six little Draculas in a row, every one with a missing front tooth.

What with the Tooth Fairy as well as stockings to fill, it was going to get pretty busy in Sarah's room this Christmas Eve.

A WORD FROM THE AUTHOR

"Just before our choir's Christmas concert, I got a huge black eye. Being the smallest, I was right in front! It inspired this story."

My Weekly

ON SALE
EVERY
TUESDAY

Super Fiction
By BIG NAME
Authors

· · · · · · · · · · · · · · · ·

Top Celebrity
Interviews

· · · · · · · · · · · · · · · ·

Real-life
Stories

· · · · · · · · · · · · · · · ·

Looking Good

· · · · · · · · · · · · · · · ·

Cookery,
Health, Travel,
Puzzles,
Fancy That!

PACKED WITH GREAT READING